The Engineer Speaks

Memoirs Covering Five Decades
Of
Highway Problems in Duval County
By
Arthur Neyle Sollee, Sr.

"No great thing is created
suddenly, any more than a bunch of
grapes or a fig. If you tell me that you
desire a fig, I answer you that there
must be time. Let it first blossom
then bear fruit, then ripen."

EPICTETUS

Dedicated

to

the memory of

my

Father and Mother

And

to my Wife

Edna R. Sollee

And

to my Children

Arthur N. Sollee, Jr.

Annette Sollee Lew

William L. Sollee

Richard P. Sollee

Katherine M. Sollee

ACKNOWLEDGEMENTS

I wish to acknowledge freely using Jacksonville's two daily newspapers for much of the data contained in Chapters XIV, XXVI and XXVIII. I am particularly appreciative of the reporting of the highway problems of Duval County by R. Michael Anderson, Charles Bermpohl, Hank Drane, Stephen W. Holland, Jere Moore, Jr., Otis Perkins, Randolph Pendleton, James R. Ward and Frank B. Young of *The Florida Times-Union* and Jane Albertson, Lloyd Brown, Reg Crowder and George Harmon of the *Jacksonville Journal*. These writers covered their assignments with enthusiasm and a dedication to accuracy.

My gratitude and thanks without reservations go to my patient and understanding wife, Edna Marie, who not only read and re-read my manuscripts but took additional time from her bridge to do all of the typing.

CONTENTS

Chapter I .... The Challenge

Chapter II .... Shall We Plan?

Chapter III .... Planning Fundamentals

Chapter IV .... The Beach Boulevard Story

Chapter V .... Duval County Beaches — A Country Road

Chapter VI .... The Forties of World War II

Chapter VII .... The Post War Era

Chapter VIII .... The Year of 1946

Chapter IX .... The Year of 1947

Chapter X .... The Year of 1948

Chapter XI .... The Year of 1949

Chapter XII .... The Year of 1950

Chapter XIII .... 1950 Bonds — From Official Statement

Chapter XIV .... The Years of 1951-1952

Chapter XV .... The Year 1953 — The McCarty Term

Chapter XVI .... The Johns Administration

Chapter XVII .... The Collins Administration Begins

Chapter XVIII .... The Formative Period of
the Jacksonville Expressway Authority

Chapter XIX .... The 1957 Revenue Bond Program

Chapter XX .... The Proposed 20th Street Bridge

Chapter XXI .... The 1963 Revenue Bond Program

Chapter XXII .... The 1963 Revenue Bond Program — In Retrospect

Chapter XXIII .... History of J. Turner Butler Boulevard

Chapter XXIV .... Some Involved Citizens

Chapter XXV .... The City Planning and Advisory Board

Chapter XXVI .... Bridges That Bind

Chapter XXVII .... The 1990 Plan

Chapter XXVIII .... Federal Bureau of Public Roads

Chapter XXIX .... The Proposed Dames Point Bridge

Chapter XXX .... The Proposed Dames Point Bridge — A Review

Chapter XXXI .... Yesteryears, Today and Tomorrow

ABOUT THE AUTHOR

Athur Neyle Sollee, Sr. was born near Tifton, Georgia on May 23, 1900. After short stays in Waycross and Savannah, Georgia his family moved to Jacksonville, Florida in 1904. He attended South Jacksonville elementary school and completed his high school education at Duval High School in 1918.

After being discharged from the United States Army in December, 1918, he was admitted to the Engineering College at the University of Florida. In 1922 he received a Bachelor of Science in Civil Engineering Degree. At graduation, he was inducted into Phi Kappa Phi, National Honorary Society. Four years later, after meeting the requirements of the College of Engineering, he received a Civil Engineer Degree from the University.

He was employed by The George B. Hills Company, Engineers, from June 1922 through 1926; from January 1927 through May 1927 by the Putnam Lumber Company; again by the Hills Company from June 1927 through September 1928 as their resident engineer on the construction of Port Everglades, Ft. Lauderdale, Florida for the Broward County Port Authority. He was appointed by the Port Authority as their Port Engineer in October 1928 in which capacity he remained through February, 1931.

He was appointed Assistant County Engineer for Duval County in April 1931 and remained in this position until his appointment as County Engineer in January, 1939. During this period he also served in the capacity as the Zoning Director.

In April, 1956 he resigned his County Engineer position to accept the appointment as Executive Director for the Jacksonville Expressway Authority, later to become the Jacksonville Transportation Authority.

After over sixteen years with the Authority he resigned November 5, 1972.

He was a past President of The Jacksonville Engineering Professions Club, is a member of the Florida Engineering Society and National Society of Professional Engineers. He also is a registered professional engineer and land surveyor.

CHAPTER I
The Challenge

Planning Duval County's roads over the past several decades has been a challenge I have spent most of my life meeting, with, I believe, more than a modicum of enthusiasm.

I have always felt more at home over a drawing board than a typewriter, though I confess to a long-standing desire to put into a readable and more concise form the almost daily records, notes and observations I have made during the many years I have been connected in one way or another with the road system of Duval County.

Consequently, when the Jacksonville City Planning and Advisory Board asked me to write a history of this very subject I required little more than a nudge of encouragement to launch me into this unfamiliar field of writing a romantic history of such unromantic things as topography, drainage and roads. But given a catalyst such as man these things take on a new meaning when made a part of the world of economics and sociological change.

There is no record prior to 1930 of any person or organization seriously concerned with the problems of growth in Duval County other than petitions presented to the Board of County Commissioners for the establishment of a new road to the town of Pablo Beach which has since become the city of Jacksonville Beach.

Ever since man began to establish permanent sites for communal living, someone has always stepped to the forefront to lead the way.

In Duval County, it was Earle P. Luce, county engineer during 1930-31. He directed the engineering department to begin the development of a coordinate map system and topographic survey of the unincorporated areas of Duval County.

The local system of plane coordinates started under Luce was later converted to that of the U.S. Coast and Geodetic Survey's Transverse Mercator grid projection, North American datum of 1927.

Topographic surveys were continued for many years and the recorded data placed Duval County in the envious position of having the finest detailed topographic maps of any county in the South. Their use has proven to be an indispensable tool in the development and utilization of vast areas in the county.

Bulletin No. 1 on the Mapping Situation in Florida, published by the engineering experiment station of the University of Florida states as follows:

"While there is a certain cost to obtaining a topographic map of the state, there is, on the other hand, an unknown but exceedingly large toll taken by the lack of such a map. This toll is levied through flood damage to highways, railroads, agricultural lands, towns and bridges, expensive preliminary surveys, fertile but idle lands, and expensive delays.

Although such a loss of money is not readily appreciated, it is correct to say that the state of Florida is paying more for the lack of such data than it would need to pay to have the surveys made."

That a topographic map is a veritable gold mine with its great store of facts will be discernible later as we delve into the records.

Every occupation has its axioms and to a county engineer designing and building roads for the needs of tomorrow, the precept of good drainage and still more good drainage, is still a good one to follow.

The enormous value of the existing topographic maps became evident during the dreadful Depression days of the '30s immediately following the enactment of the Federal Emergency Relief Act which give birth to the Civil Works Administration work program and the Works Progress Administation program. Overnight Duval County placed thousands of men at work on worthwhile drainage and road projects with a minimum of effort and a maximum of efficiency, because of the existence of these maps.

In those trying times little could it be foreseen that the digging of ditches mostly by hand in seemingly remote areas of the county would contribute so much to the county's economy during the following decades.

Today there are only a few persons who can remember the hopelessness of thousands of citizens whose only request was "give me any kind of work so that I may live and keep my family from hunger." And it was these legions of men of every race and creed who, scorning handouts and willing to work, went "belly deep" into the swamps with axes and shovels to dig hundreds of miles of ditches for the primary purpose of obtaining proper road drainage and mosquito control. But a secondary objective was obtained by this back breaking labor in the reclamation of thousands of acres of swamps, swales, and flat lands.

The purpose of the Federal Civil Works Administration and Works Progress Administration was to put men to work at something, but due to the availability of topographic maps and to good planning, the productiveness of the program changed lands of very low value to highly desirable residential, commercial and industrial property.

The public was generally aware that a huge drainage and road building program was underway in the county but what they did not know was that the office of the county engineer was the guiding hand of the Federal Works Program. Every ditch and road was located, surveyed and work supervised by someone from the county office.

The organizations of the many governmental work programs eventually became amazingly efficient in their operations in spite of the usual periodic directives from Washington.

A most astounding feature of the vast countrywide drainage and road program which continued to function for many years without any federal assistance, was the infinitesimal amount of money that was expended for the acquisition of rights of way.

The following are some of the larger drainage projects that were carefully planned by the County Engineering Department and are irrefutable proof of the inseparable value of good planning coupled with the execution of the plans as a contributing factor in the economic growth of the county.

1. The Highway Avenue drainage canal from Edgewood Avenue westerly to the north branch of Cedar Creek. Prior to the construction of this canal Edgewood Avenue and Cassat Avenue north of Lenox Avenue including the area between the two roads was subject to constant flooding with the result that many parcels of land were sold for unpaid taxes. This entire area is now highly industrialized.

2. The canal improving a tributary to Ribault River, from Kings Road southerly to Mays Road and continuing southerly toward Commonwealth Avenue. The area north of Mays Road originally was a large swamp and part pasture for a dairy, but now the site of a Seaboard Coast Line Railroad Industrial complex.

3. The series of drainage ditches from the Lane Avenue area beteen Commonwealth Avenue and Mays Road all emptying into the improved tributary canal to Ribault River.

4. The numerous canals draining the Six Mile Creek watershed being a vast area served by Pritchard Road, Jones Road, Bulls Bay Highway and Imeson Road.

5. The Murray Hill canal from Cassat Avenue near Kingsbury Avenue easterly through a highly developed residential district to Big Fishweir Creek at the Seaboard Coast Line Railroad north of Park Street.

6. Main canals and laterals excavated in the southwest section of the county principally being in the area east of Ricker Road and south of Wilson Boulevard.

7. The 5th Street canal beginning at Melson Avenue going westerly to the main north-south tributary to Ribault River. It receives the storm waters from a large area originating many city blocks east of Melson Avenue.

8. Masters Branch and feeder ditches with headwaters being in the Grand Park area all flowing into Ribault River just west of U.S. No. 1.

9. The network of road outfall ditches in the vicinity of Dunn Avenue, Duval Station Road, New Berlin Road, Starret Road, Armsdale Road and Boney Road.

10. The mile long drainage canal beginning several hundred feet east of Lake Lucina in the Arlington area emptying into the upper reaches of Red Bay Branch

to the East. The construction of this major drainage facility made it possible to efficiently develop over several hundred acres of property.

11. All major canals flowing easterly into Big Pottsburgh Creek and draining a vast area east of University Boulevard included between Beach Boulevard and Phillips Highway.*

12. The extensive series of ditches in the Loretto-Mandarin area, draining such roads as Hartley Road, Pine Acres Road, Hood Road, Loretto Road, Sunbeam Road, Mandarin Road and St. Augustine Road. The construction of these ditches included cleaning out and widening the upper reaches of Cormorant Branch, Deep Bottom Branch and Sandy Bottom Branch.

13. All of the road outfall ditches included in the area bounded on the north by Beach Boulevard, on the east by Phillips Highway and on the south and east by University Boulevard. This area is a part of Little Pottsburg Creek watershed.

14. The outfall ditches draining Hogan Road (Beach Boulevard) between Spring Glen Road and San Pablo Road.

Most of the hundreds of drainage ditches were excavated by hand as the purpose of the federal program was to give everyone an opportunity to work. The thinking was that machines would eliminate this opportunity and "higher-ups" in Washington would not entertain any advice that a more efficient program could be obtained by the use of draglines on the larger canals.

While the massive countrywide drainage program was under way, an equally large and complementary road development and improvement project was in full swing. The personnel of the county engineer's office were as busy as yellow jackets building a nest. New roads were being laid out as rights of way were being acquired at no cost to the county, many existing roads were being planned to be extended to form circumferential highways such as existing University Boulevard and surveyors were in the field executing all layout work. Simultaneously trees were being felled, underbrush cleared, grading machines were carving new roadbeds and reworking the old ones, mile after mile of earth windrows were being built with shovels and meticulously shaped in preparation for the traveling asphalt mixing plant to gobble up and mix with asphalt. The sand-asphalt mix left by the moving mixing plant was then attacked by both men and machines and within a matter of a few weeks an old graded road was transformed into a smooth paved highway.

And so, with the eager help of a thousand sweating, muscled backs the winding trails and rutted roads of the county were slowly transformed into a network of highways.

To the reader who whizzes over expressways and highways it is difficult to realize that 50 years ago it was a chore to travel to most of the outlying sections of the county. No wonder then that after each area was made more accessible to the others the economic outlook began to brighten and pride in community affairs began to emerge.

Many of the principal roads that were paved during the '30s were Cedar Point, New Berlin, Dames Point, Eastport, Duval Station, Duval, Pecan Park, Armsdale, Braddock, Thomas, Plummer, Garden Street, Jones, Bulls Bay, Picketville, Ramona, Hammond, Lane, Trout River Boulevard, Ribault River Boulevard, Cleveland, Sibbald, Gilchrist, 45th Street, Memorial Park, Herlong, part of Old Middleburg, Ricker, Firestone, Jammes, Morse, 110th Street, Ortega Farms, Hamilton, Collins, Schindler Drive, Yellow Water, Halsema, Mandarin, Loretto, Hartley, Scott Mill, Beauclerc, Hood Landing, Aladdin, Belfort, Bowden, Love Grove (University Boulevard), Spring Park, Hudnal, Bowden, Merrill, Arlington, Johnson Avenue, Ft. Caroline, St. Johns Bluff, Mt. Pleasant, Girvin, Penman, San Pablo, Old Sherry Drive, Salt Air Boulevard, and Seminole Beach. In addition practically every street in every populous subdivision was paved.

---

*Originally Philips, named after Henry Bethune Philips, first chairman of the Florida State Road Department.

County Road and Bridge Projects - 1930's

Hand excavated ditch north of Loretto Road next to Bowden property February 14, 1934

Cleaning out headwaters of Cormorant Branch north of Loretto Road with W.P.A. work force February 14, 1934

CHAPTER II
Shall We Plan?

Since the beginning of time, man has been a restless creature. He always has had the urge to settle down where he could make a living by trading with anyone who might pass by.

It was only logical then that wherever a land route reached a stream, there were some who decided this was the spot where they could carry on their particular type of business or trade with those who traveled by land or water.

Jacksonville, due to its geographical location, attracted the adventurers, the businessmen, the road builders, the railroads and water-borne commerce. It became the "end of the line" for most railroads and ocean going vessels as transportation facilities to the "hinterlands" were inadequate and mere trails. And, until recent time, Jacksonville and Duval County were actually, for all practical purposes, "The Gateway to Florida," and to many, "Jacksonville was Florida."

Today Jacksonville and Duval County are synonymous, and the "Bold New City of the South" is bursting with enthusiasm; its leaders are new but full of ideas, and optimism is in full bloom.

For the first time in the long history of Duval County, the idea of proper planning has been accepted unanimously as a must, as an essential element in the aim to achieve success in community endeavors.

In every walk of life I suspect the word "planning" is one of the most used and most popular. The housewife plans to go shopping, she plans for a meal. A man plans for a business trip, a vacation, an extension to his home, an expansion to his business.

It would indeed be a dull world if plans and planning were to be eliminated.

The subject of planning is quite an imposing topic and I am sure it has been presented and advocated under such trite titles as "Planning for the Future," "Advanced Planning," or "Master Road Plans," etc. ad infinitum. But today, such phrases can be given a more modern version in keeping with the spectacular which almost becomes routine — especially in Florida and Duval County. We can say "let us hitch our ideas to the stars" in keeping with "going to the moon" which only a few short years ago was labeled a figment of the imagination, a figure of speech. But now, not even the sky is the limit.

In our earthly scheme of things, we must absorb some of the thinking of the modern physicist, the astronauts and the space engineers. In other words, we must think big, plan big and transform ideas into realities. The paths and roads in the universe are being charted with a precision that staggers the imagination, makes one shake his head in wonder and mutter to himself, "it can't be so," but there it is.

One thing is certain: Just as certain as modern man can witness a sunrise and a sunset in the space of 24 hours, so we must resolve from now on, not to be provincial in our planning. We must gather together carefully, the data that have guided us and assisted others in executing worthwhile and proven highway systems.

Let us first come down to earth and look into the realities of the methods and procedures that are used today as guides in determining the basic data that ultimately points out desire lines of travel.

The cost of acquiring, assembling and correlating data is a costly procedure. As it is for the benefit of all the public, it should be done by a government agency, and the findings presented in a simple manner to the general public.

But why should we plan? Why should we devote time, energy and money in assembling the following simple facts?

1. Where are people living now? What are their driving habits? Where will others live in the years to come?

2. Where are the business areas located today and how and where will they expand?

3. Where are the industrial centers today? Where will they be tomorrow and where are the likely areas for new such complexes to locate and thrive?

4. Where shall cultural and recreational areas be located so that they may be enjoyed without fear of encroachment by less desirable environments?

These questions are not at all complicated and one does not have to have a working knowledge of Einstein's theory of relativity or be able to solve even a simple solution in freshman algebra in order to give fairly accurate answers.

Just as the splitting of the atom by the scientists of today has revealed some of the mysteries of the universe, so too will the geographical and topographical features of an area and their utilization by man be the keys that will open and reveal sound answers to our transportation problems. This is based upon the premise that preliminary investigations and interviews are accurate and interpretations are intelligent.

Graphic representations of transportation movements and studies of any area invariably point out the existing desire lines of travel of the people of the community. With this information it is possible to lay out predicted and more efficient desire lines of travel for periods from five to thirty or more years in the future.

It is well to bear in mind that travel routes now used are not always the most desirable ones. By using data already available and by having an intimate knowledge of the area, it is possible to define desire lines or corridors of travel.

Such desire lines of travel may be likened to a pointed shotgun that is cocked and ready to release a concentrated yet diffusible mass from its origin that is predestined to travel along fixed paths on its way to points of ultimate destination.

Duval County is experiencing a good rate of growth, in excess of the national average and therein lies our problem which must be solved by planning.

It is the duty of officials in charge of road expansion programs in their respective areas to investigate thoroughly the total transportation needs, and not confine their thinking to isolated areas.

Duval County's economy demands good roads and will require many more in the years ahead.

Why should we do all of these things? Why do we build costly transportation facilities? The answer to these questions is a simple formula. It controls the universe of man more than all of the combined formulas known to science. What is the formula? It is $T=M$ or Time equals Money.

County Road and Bridge Projects - 1930's

Timuquana Road timber bridge over Ortega River - Removing swing span - September 1936

The Timuquana Road Bridge looking east over Ortega River as it appeared on August 3, 1936

CHAPTER III
Planning Fundamentals

The Jacksonville Chamber of Commerce, the industrialists and the progressive businessmen of Duval County, in all of their extensive advertising always stress the strategic geographical location of the county. They hammer home the accessibility of the Atlantic Ocean and picture the St. Johns River meandering through the area providing easy access for oceangoing vessels. It is clearly shown that the river, with all of its many tributaries, provides the ultimate to thousands of lovers of waterfront property and to the small boat owners.

The developer and businessman, whether he is trying to sell a location or parcel for an industry, for a business or for home sites also invariably points out all of the favorable and numerous geographical and topographical features.

The planner likewise must use the basic tools of the industrialist, the businessman and the real estate developer. He also must recognize the pattern for the growth of Duval County was determined eons ago and the beginning of the utilization of this pattern was when man moved in.

Planning therefore for the development of Duval County or any other large area involves four principal factors:

1. Geographical
2. Topographical
3. Environmental
4. Political

The geographical and topographical features of Duval County are the unchangeables — for as far as man is concerned they have always been here. Geographically, it is its location with respect to the state, the southeast part of the United States, the continent, the world and its climate.

Its topography consists of the rivers and streams, its beaches, marshlands, swamps and variable highlands.

The utilization of these two unchangeables by man-made things, always sets off a chain of events and conditions which constitutes the environmental features.

These environmentals may be classified roughly as: railroad facilities, docks, heavy industries, installations by the armed forces, centers of learning, airports, office buildings, residential developments and principal highways.

Examples of some noteworthy environmentals that will have a continuing impact and effect on all phases of endeavor in Duval County are (1) the Navy installations located in the southwest section of the county and in the Mayport-Atlantic Beach area; (2) the Jacksonville International Airport; (3) the industrialization of the old Jacksonville Municipal Airport; (4) the new brewery located at

Interstate 95 and Dunn Avenue; (5) Interstate 295 and (6) the residential growth in the southeast area of the county.

Let us now go for a ride with an astronaut and as he passes over Duval County, let us take a clear picture of the county. Although Confucius is quoted as saying "A picture is worth a thousand words," it takes the mind of man to interpret and translate into words all of the significant features that are so meaningful to anyone whose objective is to help develop plans for future highway corridors.

A mental photograph reveals the following:

In the southwest section a dense residential area extends southerly from Interstate 10 toward the Clay County line. It is like a great wedge, separated by Interstate 295 and flanked on the east by the Jacksonville Naval Air Station and the west by the vast Cecil Field-Gunnery School Navy installations. Farther to the west are thinly wooded flatlands, some dairies and scattered houses.

It is evident that future good residential areas are limited and can only be extended southerly and into Clay County.

The sector of land included between Interstate 10 and U.S. 1 has some residential areas but the predominant use now and in the future will be for heavy industry, railroad yards and warehousing. The Baldwin area is mostly dependent on industry and on future railroad plans.

The pie shaped area between U.S. 1 and Main Street is largely residential with the exception of industries on the extreme fringe areas where railroad facilities are available. The magnificent and modern airport located between Lem Turner Road and Interstate 95 is a barrier that will definitely limit the northerly expansion of the existing residential areas.

The vast square-like area east of U.S. 17 (Main Street) extending to the Atlantic Ocean and north of the St. Johns River to Nassau River is sparsely settled and future residential expansion will be moderate and limited to the modest to low income groups. The marshes bisected by the Intracoastal Waterway are uninviting and commercial usage only will be in close proximity to the St. Johns River.

The state owned lands on Little Talbot Island have great possibilities but it will never reach its potential until such time as it is made more accessible from U.S. 17 near the New Berlin area by means of a multi-land divided highway. Water supply of course will dictate the extent of development.

The entire north side of the St. Johns River from Trout River at Main Street east to the Atlantic Ocean offers an unparalleled potential to every phase of the maritime industry, which could be enhanced by a modern divided highway constructed due east from U.S. 17 located along a corridor south of and generally parallel to the range line between township one north and one south.

This new highway would permit the development of Broward River as far north as Cedar Bay Road as a deep and calm magnificent adjunct to the choppy, current prone St. Johns River. This would necessitate the construction of a movable highway bridge over the river at Heckscher Drive. If this were done, then all of the Imeson Airport tract by proper planning could have access to deep water which would top the list as prime industrial sites as rail and highway are already available and the new jet airport only minutes away. The new highway would then serve a dual purpose by being extended to Little Talbot Island.

The remaining area of Duval County is seen as a great wooded area extending southerly and easterly from the St. Johns River to St. Johns County and to the Atlantic Ocean. Within a six-mile radius of the Jacksonville City Hall is a high density residential area extending from the Arlington section southerly to Deerwood and then westerly and southwesterly to the St. Johns River and the San Jose, Mandarin-Loretto area.

The beach areas are highly developed along a relatively narrow stretch from North Atlantic Beach south through Neptune Beach and Jacksonville Beach and can only expand westward and southerly into St. Johns County.

Mayport Naval Air Station, the home of the South Atlantic Fleet on the southside of the St. Johns River with frontage on the Atlantic Ocean is another governmental agency that has changed the former sleepy ways of the Mayport area to an active and constantly growing force in the beaches economy.

This southeast area of Duval County contains at least twice as much land available for residential expansion than exists for a like purpose in the remainder of the county.

It has been recognized by many for some time and it has been publicly stated by the writer for many years that the residential trend in Duval is to the east and southeast.

The construction of the many bridges from the north and west sides of the river to the south and east sides of the river is mute testimony as to what is going on in the community.

Several reasons given as to why this trend is to the east and southeast areas are its climate, its relatively close proximity and easy access to downtown Jacksonville and the beaches and particularly the absence of heavy industry which produces noxious odors, fumes, gases and noise.

Mr. "Average Citizen," who has a good overall knowledge of the community, can always check the practicability of any proposed large scale expressway-bridge project by following an elementary rule which is, that the determining factor in the location of highways for large volumes of traffic is to build within a corridor that will bring people from areas of high residential occupancy to those areas where the same people make a living —in other words, from where one sleeps to where one works. It is just that simple.

The fourth factor — political — is always present. It lurks in the background and hides behind a multitude of elements that are as varied as the colors in Joseph's coat. It is more deceptive than a star halfback and more elusive than a tiger in the jungles of India and by far more dangerous.

The political force is masterminded by the proverbial "man-behind-the-scenes" who transmits his orders in person or by telephone.

Who is this political figure? How does he operate? What are his motives and what effect does his manipulating have on the community?

It would be very easy to name names and bring out a well kept diary that has been in the making for many years and answer all of the above queries, but as Longfellow said, "let the dead past bury its dead," and this shall be done.

Jacksonville and Duval County are no different from any other like community in these United States, for political bossism has always been part of the American way of life. In some instances it has been a benevolent ruler, but to the everlasting shame of our community life, local "bosses" have been greedy, selfish, become wealthy and been ruthless with those who dared oppose their philosophy as it affected the orderly processes of government. They have acted as individuals and on some occasions have been known to combine forces like jackals seeking a kill.

The "boss" more than likely takes an active part in the life of the community, is a member of various civic and professional organizations, contributes generously to charities and ever so generously to political campaigns — and he or his organization always represents in one way or another an individual or some type of business, company or corporation that does business with one or more governmental bodies or is subject to decisions of these bodies.

The "boss" is the great deceiver and tempter. He is the one who embryonic elected officials are led to believe, exerts great influence with the voters and can "swing" elections. Without thinking, these officials swallow the "hook and line" and as long as they "jump through the hoop" are weighed down with the lead sinker of servitude. And once hooked, the official "fish" is fed the crumbs while the "boss" goes on his merry way, ever seeking new material for his docile and captured bowl of exhibitionists.

The "captured exhibitionists" always do the bidding of their master and by their decisions the interests of the public are relegated to the background, and substitute proposals are brought forth that hide their real identity and purpose by being clothed with colorful words that sparkle and shine to blind the unsuspecting.

The "boss" sits in the driver's seat and with self-aggrandizement, chuckles with satisfaction at the stupidity of his "captured fish", for in one way or another his edicts will directly or indirectly bring in a flow of public funds, satisfy his ego, or delay and block some worthwhile public function on which he has not been able to "horn in on."

Such a man can be the direct cause of losses to the community in millions of dollars and the reverse would be true if he did not live a double standard.

What a pity the mind of such persons as the "boss" could not be directed to those channels that would best serve his community and fellow man.

Every community is afflicted by "bosses" and every community loses by their actions through the machinations of subservient elected henchmen. And when the voice and ideas of a devil's advocate has dared make public his views, he has been warned to cease and desist or his job or position would be in jeopardy.

It is the prayerful hope of the engineer and planner that maybe someday the subtle influence and interference of the "bosses" will be a forgotten memory and that honest differences in the thinking of all those dedicated to the pursuit of planning in Jacksonville and Duval County may be resolved by meetings "in the sunshine."

County Road and Bridge Projects - 1930's

Looking North on Love Grove Road (now University Blvd. South) from Hogan Road (now Beach Blvd.) April 13, 1936

Bowden Road looking East from Salisbury Road. Skinners Dairy to right. February 2, 1934

Love Grove Road (now University Blvd. West) and Bowden Road looking east across the Florida East Coast tracks as of June 10, 1936

CHAPTER IV
The Beach Boulevard Story

The construction of Atlantic Boulevard from South Jacksonville to the beaches was in its final phase, but many citizens, especially those living in old Pablo Beach, Hogan and South Jacksonville, were already thinking of another route to the beaches.

The route they had in mind would link Hogan and the Big Pottsburg Creek area with Third Street on the beaches. Petitions requesting surveys for this route were presented to the County Commission as early as April, 1923. A year later the commission authorized the first of these surveys which were to extend over the following four or five years. In each of the surveys the proposed road began at Hogan Road and ended in the south end of what is now Jacksonville Beach.

It was to remain a dream, a paper highway, for most of the next decade until 1932, when the then County Engineer, Earl P. Luce learned from a Florida East Coast Railroad official that the company planned to abandon its branch line to Mayport. Luce realized immediately that purchase of the right of way of this line would provide the county with a perfect route for the second road to the beaches.

Even before the railroad removed its track, Luce, on March 3, 1932, had a field party (which included me) establish the location of the right of way by marking its center line with iron piping. This was to eliminate any possibility of future dispute over the accuracy employed in locating the property. The survey took just four days but Luce was to spend the remainder of his days trying unsuccessfully to persuade the county to buy the old right of way. When he died, July 4, 1932, his successor J. A. Long continued advocating using the old railroad as the best and most economical second route to the beaches, until, in the early part of 1937, the county bought the entire right of way from Atlantic Boulevard to 3rd Street on the beaches and Mayport, for just $8,500. An additional 50 foot of right of way on both sides of the old track was deeded to the county free of charge by the adjoining property owners, the Swallow Hopkins interests and the Pitts family. This 8.2 miles of free right of way began near what is now Southside Boulevard and ended at the Intracoastal Waterway.

The same year the Legislature incorporated the newly acquired highway route into the state road system, naming it State Road 376.

In September of that year the county asked the state to begin construction of the highway. Then, without waiting for the state to move, the county commission approved construction of the new road under the federal Works Progress Administration. Work on the $1.6 million project began in 1938, with slightly less than one-third of the cost being borne by the federal government.

The work, much of which was done by hand, came to a halt when all W.P.A.

The Beaches in the 1930's and 1940's

Looking north from Duval St. Johns County Line. Erosion due to storms has exposed peat. June, 1934

Beach at low tide - Jacksonville Beach Pier in distance. Note Autos on Beach July 4, 1933

Looking north from Duval-St. Johns County Line. Note sand ridge on beach due to Southeast winds.
August, 1932.

work was suspended in the fall of 1941. The county immediately asked the State Road Department to continue with the project, but America's entry into World War II, just a matter of weeks away, banished all thought of completing it until the war was over.

From almost the very beginning of the project the County Commission had pledged its full cooperation and all of the county's surplus gas tax revenue in support of it. As a result of this pledge practically all of the state's share of this money was also used for the road's construction. Designated Beach Boulevard by the county as early as June 1939, the name was adopted by the State Road Department in October 1946.

So, seventeen years after the idea was first conceived by Luce, the new road, a magnificent four-lane expressway, was opened to traffic on December 17, 1949 with the dedication of the B. B. McCormick Bridge over the Intracoastal Waterway. The dream, the paper highway, was finally a reality.

The Beaches in the 1930's and 1940's

Steel Avenue looking east toward Atlantic Ocean. October 19, 1935.

County Commissioner Howard Belote standing in back of Atlantic Beach concrete seawall after destructive September 1947 storm.

Just completed Florida Works Progresses Administration Seawall in Neptune Beach just south of Atlantic Boulevard Ramp. June, 1937

CHAPTER V

Duval County Beaches-A County Road

At one time the beaches of Duval County were considered as a county responsibility and therefore eligible for maintenance as a county road.

Such was the thinking in the 1930's and 1940's.

If debris or dead fish were washed upon the strand, the county commissioners were called upon to remove all such obstructions that were hazardous to beach auto traffic.

And too, the Duval County sheriff's motorcycle road patrol maintained law and order on the beaches from the St. Johns County line north to the south jetty.

During the frequent stormy periods, when the ocean's fury washed away the sand, destroyed bulkheads and threatened the adjacent houses, the county was asked to help ease the destructive forces of the sea. They responded by sending several crews of convict labor that worked many times all night filling sacks with sand and erecting them to form a temporary restraint to the battering forces of the waves.

It was taken for granted by the residents having property fronting the Atlantic, that it was the duty of the county to protect them from the periodic ravages of the sea.

Likewise, it became the responsibility of the office of the county engineer to supervise the maintenance of the beaches as part of the county road system.

As the assistant county engineer in the '30s and county engineer in the '40s, I studied problems involving the erosion of the beaches, its causes and possible solutions.

If the beaches were considered as an integral part of the county network of roads and if the beaches could be maintained as a readily useful artery for automobiles, then at the same time damage to beachfront property could be held to a minimum.

With this in mind, intensive studies of reports and records of the U.S. Corps of Engineers revealed that the corps had acknowledged that in some instances the possible cause of excessive beach erosion was the jetties at river entrances.

The hydraulics of the currents and runouts of the Atlantic Ocean a little offshore, from the south jetty, south to the St. Johns County line, appeared to be accentuated by the jetties which caused above normal erosion, particularly during periodic storms and when the tide was ebbing.

My research and interest in the preservation of the beaches as a county highway were recognized, for in April, 1935, I was appointed by Governor Dave Sholtz as a member of the Florida delegation to attend the National Rivers and Harbors Congress in Washington, D.C., May 2 and 3.

At this meeting I submitted the following resolution:

To Delegates, National River and Harbors Congress:

A proposed resolution, that if approved and adopted at this annual meeting of the National Rivers and Harbors Congress, will be a definite step toward the obtaining of federal studies for a hitherto comparatively neglected but essential feature of our coasts and harbor entrances.

WHEREAS, the chief of engineers under the secretary of war is charged by law with the duty of making preliminary examinations and surveys looking to the improvement of harbor and inlet entrances as may from time to time be ordered by Congress; and

WHEREAS, such improvements when, if and as made have an effect on the shoreline adjacent to such harbor and inlet entrances;

NOW, THEREFORE, BE IT RESOLVED, that the Chief of Engineers, U.S. Army, be requested, in his studies and reports relating to improvements of harbors and inlet entrances to include information concerning the configuration of the shoreline and the probable effect thereon, that may be expected to result from the improvement, having particular reference to erosion and/or accretion for a distance of not less than ten (10) miles on either side of said entrance.

Submitted by

Arthur N. Sollee,
Jacksonville, Florida
Member of Florida Delegation
National Rivers and Harbors Congress

Knowing the influence of the political arena in the Capitol, I solicited and received the aid of Florida U.S. Senator Duncan U. Fletcher.

It was through the senator's influence the foregoing resolution was adopted and later included in the United States Code, Annotated, 1937 Cumulative Annual Pocket Part, Title 33, Navigation and Navigable Waters, Page 74, Paragraph 546a.

Paragraph 546a reads as follows:

SEC. 4. "Every report submitted to Congress in pursuance of any provision of law for preliminary examination and survey looking to the improvement of the entrance at the mouth of any river or at any inlet, in addition to other information which the Congress has directed shall be given, shall contain information concerning the configuration of the shoreline and the probable effect thereon that may be expected to result from the improvement having particular reference to erosion and/or accretion for a distance of not less than 10 miles on either side of the said entrance."

The Beaches in the 1930's and 1940's

Under the Atlantic Beach Pier looking south. June 17, 1934

Looking south from prolongation of 16th Street, Atlantic Beach. Note debris on beach. June 17, 1934

Looking south from Atlantic Boulevard Ramp, June 14, 1934

Note that the 10 miles mentioned in Paragraph 546a correspond to the approximate 10 mile distance from the St. Johns River south jetty to the St. Johns County line.

As beach erosion increased and damages mounted after each successive storm, in desperation the officials of Atlantic Beach, Neptune Beach and Jacksonville Beach turned to the Duval County commissioners for help.

Their concern was motivated by the desire to not only keep the beaches suitable for automobile traffic but to protect the oceanfront property.

The county commission, not having funds or a ready solution, directed me to write to the local U.S. Corps of Engineers about Duval County beach problems and request the assistance of the federal government in solving an ever worsening situation.

Following is the text of the letter sent to the district engineer:

May 17, 1948

Willis E. Teale, Colonel,
District Engineer,
Corps of Engineers,
Jacksonville, Florida.

In re: Erosion of Beaches of
Duval County, Florida

Dear Sir:

During the past fifteen years considerable apprehension has arisen among the property owners of the beaches of Duval County over the extensive erosion which is increasing from year to year and its effect on millions of dollars worth of property. Due to the rapid increase in the use of these beaches and the construction of dwellings facing the ocean, the problem of erosion is now one of serious proportions. As in other parts of the United States where the beaches are continuously being dissipated by the agencies of the ocean, the beaches of Duval County have been under this incessant attack, and the property owners, as well as the hundreds of thousands of visitors, are afraid that within a short period of time the beaches will disappear and driving no longer may be possible. The beaches of Duval County have always been known for their excellent driving quality and this one asset appears to be headed for destruction caused by the forces of the ocean.

In order to properly evaluate the conditions of the beaches of Duval

County it will be necessary to dwell briefly on the theory of the origin and construction of these beaches. According to James H. C. Martens in his pamphlet entitled *Beaches of Florida*, "The original source of the sand in Florida, including that on the beaches, is to be found in the Piedmont and Appalachian Mountain regions of the southeastern states, where sand has been and is being formed by the gradual decay of various hard rocks exposed to the disintegrating action of the atmosphere. Sand which has been carried down to the sea by the Savannah, Altamaha and other rivers of Georgia and the Carolinas is gradually shifted to the southward by the shore currents and wave action along the Atlantic Coast. Thus there is a constant replenishing of the supply of sand on the east coast of Florida."

According to all available surveys made by both private parties and the federal government there was a more or less stabilized condition of Duval County beaches prior to the construction of the St. Johns River jetties and the dredging of the channel between the jetties. As the jetties have progressively been improved and made impervious to the action of the tides and currents, the erosion of the beaches has been aggravated proportionally. The deepening and improvements of the channel of the St. Johns River from Jacksonville to the ocean has also contributed materially to the erosion of the beaches south of the south jetties, by reason of the marked increase in the velocity and volume of water passing through the jetties.

In November and December 1932, the beaches of Duval County, south of the jetties were lowered from 2 to 4½ feet along the greater parts of this particular section of the beach, which condition was caused by a storm originating in the Atlantic arising in the vicinity of Bermuda. This storm was accompanied by extremely high tides and large waves which reached the shore in advance of high winds. The maximum wind velocity was reported to have reached approximately fifty miles per hour. The destructive damage due to this storm, figuratively speaking, set off a series of investigations to determine why the beaches were eroding so rapidly and if there could be any remedy. As a result of requests made by Duval County and the Jacksonville Beach towns, the U.S. government made an investigation to determine the damage done and to seek the cause if such were possible. A report was rendered to the district engineer under date of December 29, 1932 by an associate engineer of the local U.S. engineer office in which all pertinent data and observations were presented covering Duval County beaches and others in Florida. Unfortunately the report did not place its finger on any contributing factor as the

The Beaches in the 1930's and 1940's

Fifteenth Street ramp, Atlantic Beach. Looking south from the north line of 15th Street. September 16, 1934

Looking South from Atlantic Beach 15th Street ramp. February 4, 1934

Looking north from Jacksonville Beach Amusement Pier July 4, 1933

cause of this extensive erosion nor did it present any possible solution to the problem.

The county engineer department shortly thereafter was requested by many interested property owners at the Beaches to make a study of the conditions. It was the conclusion of the engineer department of the county that although the storm was the material cause of the damage it was greatly accentuated by the St. Johns River jetties. Under date of April 15, 1933, the Beach Erosion Board Office of the Chief of Engineer, U.S. Army issued an Interim Report. I wish to quote from this report as follows:

"**Inlets:** In the vicinity of an inlet new forces come into play. Tidal currents move through the entrance and may be quite powerful if there is a large tidal prism fed through the inlet. On flood tide the tendency is for converging currents to flow into the inlet from all directions. Hence there exists, not only an inflowing current along the axis of the inlet, but also inflowing current moving nearly parallel to the adjacent beaches. On ebb tide, on the contrary, the tendency is for the water to flow straight out to sea in a more concentrated stream. The ebb may set up eddies or counter currents under the lee of each of the two points with the result that on ebb tide also, there may be currents along these beaches directed toward the inlet.

"On the leeward side, on the contrary, the tendency of the current induced by the inlet on flood tide, (and often also on ebb tide) is opposed to the prevailing direction of littoral current. There may then be a local reversal of that current, at some or all tidal stages, in the vicinity of the inlet, and a resumption of the normal direction further down the coast." This is the condition that exists to the south of the St. Johns River Inlet.

Quoting again from this Interim Report:
"**Erosion to leeward of long high jetties.** It is generally recognized that where there is a well defined resultant movement of sand along the beach in one direction, the construction of a jetty or series of jetties of such size as to impound the littoral drift will RESULT in erosion of the LEEWARD position. In the numerous instances where such erosion has occurred, it is obvious that the amount of sand

taken away from the leeward eroding area, by littoral drift or
other cause, was greater than the amount transported to the
beach from the floor of the ocean or from any other source."

Quoting further from this report 6/37
Conclusion: "The most important conclusion from the
practical viewpoint of those designing beach protective
structures is that the sea bottom off shore cannot be counted
on as a source of beach building material."

After this Interim Report was studied by the engineer department of
Duval County it appeared that the only solution and remedy of the
situation would be some type of federal aid. Therefore with this in
view a tentative proposal was drawn up looking to the improvements
which only the federal government could grant. A proposed bill was
duly presented to the Honorable Senator Fletcher of Florida who
followed through and had the bill passed in both houses that would
enable the U.S. engineers to take into consideration erosion of the
coast line when making studies for constructing jetties and dredging
inlets. The law may be found in "The Code of the Laws of the U.S. of
America; Title 33 Navigation and Navigable Waters, Paragraph 546-
A." "Every report submitted to Congress in pursuance of any
provisions of law for preliminary examination and survey looking to
the improvements of the entrance at the mouth of any river or at any
inlet, in addition to other information which the Congress has directed
shall be given, shall contain information concerning the configuration
of the shoreline and the possible effect thereon that may be expected
to result from the improvement having particular reference to erosion
and or accretion for a distance of not less than 10 miles on either side
of the said entrance." Again note that the distance from the south jetty
of the St. Johns River inlet to the Duval County-St. Johns County line
is approximately 10 miles.

To further substantiate Duval County's claim that the jetties are
causing erosion to the beaches south of said jetties, I wish to quote
from a paper presented December 5, 1927, at Jacksonville, Florida by
Col. Mark M. Brooke, District Engineer of the Jacksonville District,
U.S. Engineer Department, at a meeting of the Shore and Beach
Preservation Association: "I understand that the erosion of Palm Beach
has been more marked since the improvement of the inlet at the north
end of the beach connecting the sound behind the beach (called Lake
Worth) with the ocean. An engineer who has given this problem some
thought is of the opinion that the jetties arrest the littoral drift from
the north and that the swift ebb tide between these jetties carries this

The Beaches in the 1930's and 1940's

Jacksonville Beach at low tide. Note: Jacksonville Beach Amusement Pier upper right. November 1932 storm.

Looking south towards Jacksonville Beach Amusement Pier. Note Life Saving Corps Guard on duty. July 4, 1933

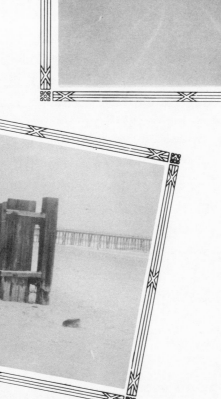

Man standing by remains of old timber bulkhead 14 feet west of existing bulkhead. Looking north from south end of Atlantic Beach Hotel property. Hotel pier right center. Photo taken June 2, 1933.

sand so far off shore that it does not reach the beach to the south. The beach being consequently subject to some erosion, and deprived of the necessary replacement material, is gradually being depleted. If this theory is correct it is one place where jetties are having an adverse effect on the adjacent beach." This is exactly what is happening to Duval County beaches.

Therefore since in official documents members of the U.S. engineers have conceded that the construction of jetties in the improvements of inlets (comparable to the St. Johns River improvements) is a material factor in the cause of erosion to the leeward side of inlets, then it is most apparent that the remedy lies in the federal government.

One solution, although not a permanent one, would be the replacement of the beaches, by dredging from that large shoal area immediately south of and adjacent to the south jetties. Just as the channels and rivers are dredged and maintained so could the beach in this vicinity be replenished with sand when needed under this same river and harbor improvement setup.

Another factor which would lessen the erosive powers of the current and waves would be the construction of permeable groynes, of creosote timber piling placed and designed in a manner comparable to fishing piers and amusement piers that have been in use at Atlantic Beach and Jacksonville Beach for many years. The spacing of the piling, distance between piers or groynes and the length of the piers projecting into the ocean could be determined only after extensive surveys by the U.S. engineer's office. Observations over a period of years have shown that for certain distances south of the two piers, the erosive powers of the ocean have not been as marked as on other portions of the beaches. The arresting of the littoral current by the pier piling has been the cause of these sections of the beach holding their own.

It is contended that the federal government has an interest in the usable beaches of the nation and under this premise, the U.S. engineers are earnestly requested to give favorable consideration to the end that the beaches of Duval County may be returned to a semblance of its former status and may be given protection in as far as human efforts are possible.

Respectfully submitted,   By _____
Board of County Commissioners,   Arthur N. Sollee,
Duval County, Florida.   County Engineer

It is believed the contents of this letter to Colonel Teale also speaks to the beach problems as they exist at this writing.

The Beaches in the 1930's and 1940's

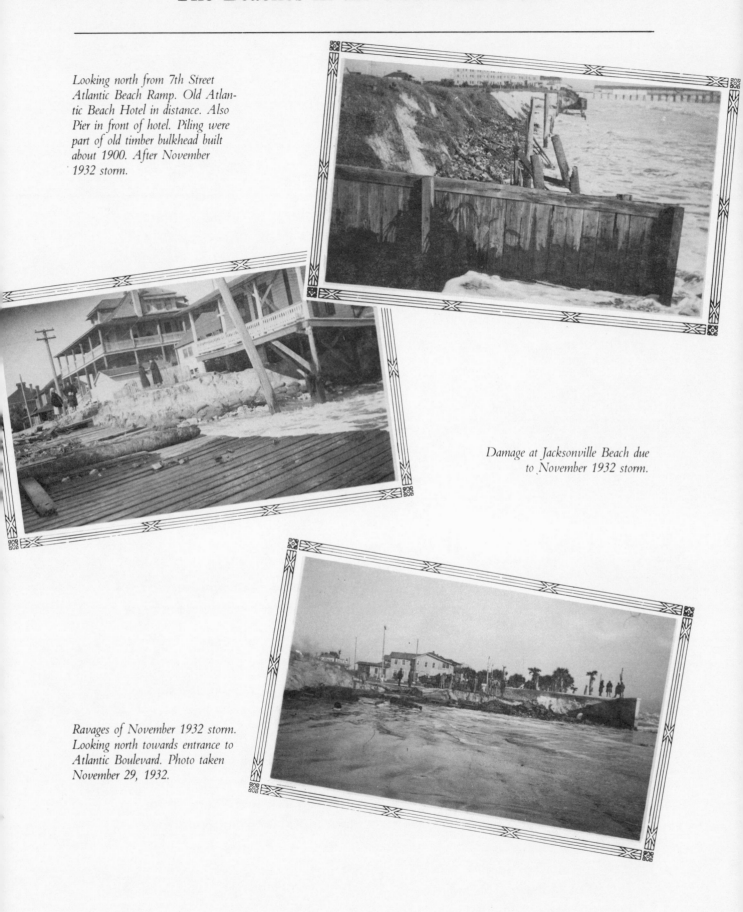

Looking north from 7th Street Atlantic Beach Ramp. Old Atlantic Beach Hotel in distance. Also Pier in front of hotel. Piling were part of old timber bulkhead built about 1900. After November 1932 storm.

Damage at Jacksonville Beach due to November 1932 storm.

Ravages of November 1932 storm. Looking north towards entrance to Atlantic Boulevard. Photo taken November 29, 1932.

CHAPTER VI

The Forties of World War II

World War II reached deep into the hearts and minds of Duval County residents with the establishment of the Jacksonville Naval Air Station, Camp Blanding and Mayport Carrier Base. Overnight Duval County became road conscious in its desire to better serve the three military establishments, particularly, since 3,260 acres of the land for Jacksonville Naval Air Station had been acquired by the Duval County Air Base Authority.

Military vehicles were everywhere. Convoys rumbled through the city to destinations unknown. It soon became apparent the highways and streets of the '30s were woefully inadequate and could not take care of the new and increasing traffic demands.

The Board of County Commissioners moved swiftly. It proposed the construction of a defense highway to Camp Blanding by way of Edgewood Avenue, Cassat Avenue and Old Orange Park Road to the Clay County line. From here it would continue southerly through Clay County and on to Camp Blanding. After this new arterial highway was built by the state it relieved considerably the congestion on U.S. 17 at the Naval Air Station.

The State Road Department with the cooperation of the county and city of Jacksonville also constructed a new four lane highway paralleling the Atlantic Coast Line Railroad from McDuff Avenue to the Naval Air Station. During the planning stage for this highway, in December 1940, county officials made strenuous efforts to obtain a fixed high level span for a new Ortega River Bridge so that boats could pass under it without halting motor traffic. Appeals were made to the commanding officer of the Naval Air Station and to U.S. Army engineers but they proved futile and a low level draw span was built. Gilchrist Stockton, a prominent citizen, was a prime figure in the movement that obtained this great traffic facility which was dedicated as Roosevelt Boulevard. Within a short time Roosevelt Boulevard was designated as U.S. 17. This brought the southwest setion of Duval County and Orange Park within minutes of downtown Jacksonville.

After many conferences with the State Road Department and Navy personnel, the federal government finally participated in the construction by the State Road Department of a two lane road from Atlantic Boulevard to the Mayport Carrier Base. The county did all of the legwork in acquiring a 100 foot right of way for this much needed road to the base and to the town of Mayport.

County Commissioner Joe F. Hammond, known throughout Florida as "Uncle Joe," was a man of firm conviction who disliked taking no for an answer if he was convinced he was right and his thinking was for the benefit of all of Duval County. As an example, notwithstanding previous setbacks for the erection of a bridge to Arlington, in the summer of 1940 he again began to seek ways to build this long sought-for connection to the beaches.

As county engineer I was directed by the county commission in January 1941 to make a survey for the proposed river span as well as define the approaches from downtown Jacksonville and connections to Atlantic Boulevard.

On Thursday, April 13, 1941 the county commissioners directed their attorney J. Henry Blount to prepare a bill for the state Legislature which would enable the county to issue revenue bonds for the span.

On Monday night May 20, 1941 in the Roosevelt Hotel at a mass meeting called by the commission to discuss the proposed Arlington Bridge, three hundred people gathered and unanimously endorsed the project. They urged the commissioners to send immediately to the county's legislative delegation a bill that would permit a toll bridge to be built. The delegation had requested the public meeting to "demonstrate the bridge is a matter of public necessity."

Assured of public support for the bridge, the delegation secured passage of the bill which permitted the county to erect the span as soon as financing became available.

The next step taken by the commission was to authorize consulting engineer John Reynolds and me to go to Washington "at the proper time" to seek federal funds.

But the "proper time" never materialized.

The city council appointed a special traffic committee made up of the following members: Honorable George C. Blume, mayor; Honorable Clyde Cannon, councilman; Honorable Fred M. Valz, commissioner; Honorable T. C. Imeson, commissioner; Honorable Tom Marshall, county commissioner; Mr. Rex Crosdell, Chamber of Commerce; Mr. Ted Bayley, Junior Chamber of Commerce; Mr. George Simons, city planner; Mr. W. E. Sheddan, city engineer; Mr. Arthur N. Sollee, county engineer; Mr. Nathan Weil, Kiwanis Club; Mr. T. C. Prince, Lions Club; Mr. T. T. Phillips, Advertising Club; Mr. Stephen Fifield, Exchange Club; Mr. Roy Schroder, administrator, W.P.A.; Mr. Earl Jones, *Florida Times-Union;* Mr. Henning Heldt, *Jacksonville Journal;* Colonel L. E. Goodrich, Camp Blanding; Major Erwin Mehlinger, Naval Air Station; and Honorable James R. Boyd, Jr., councilman, chairman.

After several months of study a report was submitted on May 13, 1941 to the president of the city council with the request that copies be made available to all interested parties. This report is reproduced here in its entirety.

FOREWARD

Jacksonville, Florida, like almost every American city over the age of twenty-one years is threatened with a malady known today as "municipal traffic blight." On May 1, 1901, because of inadequate fire protection and other circumstances, many municipal ills which existed at that time were permanently cured. From the ashes of this terrible fire arose one of the great cities of America and one of the most important distribution centers of the southeast. Trunk lines of the great rail systems spread from here, their "miles of steel ribbon" to the industrial cities of the east and midwest; to the wheat fields of the prairie states and to the "placid waters" which the intrepid Balboa in awe and wonder called "the Pacific." Sailing vessels and steamships entered the harbor and discharged their cargoes from domestic and foreign ports. Here was gathered and centered for trans-shipment by rail and water products of the state and the South. To Jacksonville came men with courage, vision and ability to make this their home: men who pitted their fortunes and abilities on the future development of Jacksonville. And so, Jacksonville arose "Phoenix-like" from its ashes to become the "Gate City" of Florida.

In those early days, while awaiting their cargoes, the top-masts of scores of vessels, with furled sails, placidly rose and fell with the tides of the St. Johns. Long freight trains moved slowly "in and out" of the yards depositing their loads at docks or terminals. Merchants and citizens alike walked to their work, or rode bicycles, street cars or buggies. Everything was comfortable, no hustle, bustle or rush. Jacksonville was growing — they were happy! No one in those good old days dreamed of 1941. No one ever dreamed that "ole Dobbin," wearing his "straw hat," and "fly-netting" would ever be called upon to give up his "municipal drinking fountains" at Bay and Main, State and Main or Main and 8th Streets.

No kid ever dreamed that he would lay aside his "sling-shot" and "air rifle" to quit shooting English sparrows on Main Street, because "ole Dobbin" would be gone, and the sparrows with him. No young couple riding their bicycles in Riverside or Springfield parks on Sunday ever dreamed or cared what 1941 would be like. Wouldn't the new model "bike" be just a "pippin?"

Weren't those town people who bought those R.E.O.'s, Columbias, Wintons and Regal autos just a bunch of fools? Didn't everyone have a great time "ribbing" them? Didn't all the neighbors have to push them blocks, or crank for hours to get them started? Didn't "ole Dobbin" have to pull her out of the sand any time they got out of the wagon rut?

Whoever dreamed that the "horseless" carriage would become in just a few years the Gargantua of commerce? Whoever dreamed that modes of travel would be so vitally affected in so short a span of time?

Today, 1941, is the motor age, and the traffic blight age. Jacksonville, like almost every other city in the United States is threatened with traffic blight — internal congestion and stagnation of commerce due to inadequate traffic facilities, controls and planning.

Down the main streets struggles a large volume of trucks, cars and pedestrians — tourist traffic, mixed with would-be shoppers cruising to find parking space. Delays to local traffic are bad for the community — delays to through traffic are bad for the economic life of the whole region.

What is the cost of the traffic blight? Any citizen can judge himself the disorganization of the traffic flow which is the commercial lifeblood of Jacksonville. How long does it take you to find a convenient place to park? To make even the shortest journey? To shop? To call at your bank? Or lawyer's office? Or beauty salon? Or go to the movies? Or dentist?

Research shows clearly the tremendous financial cost of unarrested deterioration. As the center of any city stagnates, business drains away. Real estate values fall. Rentals decline. Tax values shrink. The old business area loses its grip — millions are lost and thousands suffer daily as traffic blight closes in.

"Ribbon" developments of business radiating from the main center are no lasting solution. Neither are regional or suburban business centers, growing up like Topsy, as the old business centers decay because, in similar absence of careful planning, these developments in turn bring about their own strangulation and drag down property values in adjacent residential sections.

Traffic conditions in Jacksonville can be cured if a concerted and a continued attack is made upon the problem. Careful planning on a "five" year program should be commenced at once, involving "good" engineering, namely engineering without political favoritism or reward at the public expense. Business officials should work together in close harmony and understanding of the ultimate goal. (Here we can pause to pay tribute to the Jacksonville merchants and businessmen who fully realize the problem, for their fine cooperation extended to the committee).

Today is the motor age, and out of its chaotic effect upon "ole Dobbins," avenues and streets, an era of expansion and great improvements is upon Jacksonville. The traffic blight is a blessing in disguise, and from it will blossom in splendor a greater Jacksonville.

Respectfully submitted,

James R. Boyd, Jr., Chairman   Erwin Mehlinger
Arthur N. Sollee   Rex Crosdell
Nathan Weil   Henning Heldt

"Special Traffic Committee"
DIGEST

I. Purpose of Committee:

    A. To make report, after sufficient study on the traffic conditions now existing in Jacksonville, with a view of relieving the present traffic conditions as an emergency.

    B. To present to the city council and other governing bodies a long range view of improving conditions in Jacksonville for the several years to come.

II. Meetings:

    A. Regular meetings were held commencing on February 14th and every Friday thereafter until March 28th.

III. Recommendations:

    A. To establish an arterial highway loading into the city of Jacksonville, tourist information bureaus and guidance map for motorists.

    B. Engineering:

        1. Recommendations:

            a. Coordination of the city and county engineering departments in view of synchronizing the relation of city streets to county roads and highways.

            b. It is recommended that a study be given of proposal to make an aerial survey of the city of Jacksonville, Florida, in view of further and future study to be had in connection with straightening out existing traffic bottlenecks, etc.

            c. It is recommended that Beaver Street be opened up as a heavy duty arterial highway to Talleyrand Avenue.

               It is further recommended that additional land be acquired for widening Talleyrand Avenue to a 100 foot right of way, for future port developments of Jacksonville.

    C. Traffic Signals:

        1. Improvement of traffic signals now located on Broad Street Viaduct and St. Johns River Bridge.

        2. Recommendation was made that additional semaphore lights be added on the viaduct and St. Johns River Bridge in order to keep traffic in proper lanes.

    D. Parking and no parking: (In view of the fact that the streets of Jacksonville were laid out during the "horse and buggy days," the present existing metropolitan streets of Jacksonville are inadequate to properly handle traffic in its present method of usage.)

1. Recommendations:

    a. Recommend that no parking be permitted on Main Street from State Street to the St. Johns River Bridge between the hours of 8:00 A.M. and 6:30 P.M.

    b. Recommend that no parking be permitted on Forsyth Street from Broad Street to Ocean Street between 8:00 A.M. and 6:30 P.M.

    c. Recommended that no parking be permitted on Adams Street from Broad Street to Ocean Street, between 8:00 A.M. and 6:30 P.M.

    d. Recommended that no parking be permitted on Broad Street from Bay Street to State Street, between 8:00 A.M. and 6:30 P.M. That no angle parking be permitted on Broad Street at any time. (Modification to the full application of the rule should be deferred until streets intersecting Broad Street have been widened to allow areas for normal business parking.)

    e. Recommended that no parking be permitted on Beaver Street from the viaduct to Myrtle Avenue.

    f. Recommended that angle parking at the intersection of Atlantic Blvd. and Phillips Highway be eliminated; also parking angular be eliminated at 8th and Main Streets. This constitutes a great hazard to all traffic passing this area.

E. Legislative:

That the City Council pass an ordinance making it a misdemeanor for any city official or employee to "fix" or attempt to "fix a traffic ticket," after one having been given by a traffic officer.

F. Business Deliveries:

It was recommended that the various business concerns in the city of Jacksonville try to make deliveries in such a manner as not to create congested traffic in the business area of Jacksonville, and that said deliveries be made with this in view.

G. Pedestrian Control:

It is recommended that pedestrian control should be given additional study as pedestrians are at a great disadvantage in moving with or against the traffic. Suggestions were made that a study of the Washington, D.C. pedestrian traffic should be given.

H. Law Enforcement:

It is recommended that the traffic officers and police of the city of Jacksonville enforce traffic laws in regard to double parking and other infractions of law which tend to retard the uniform flow of traffic.

I. Municipal Parking Areas:

The city at this time should lay out a program for establishing municipal parking areas at regular intervals throughout the metropolitan area of Jacksonville. That traffic in the future will not tend to decrease but will continue to increase as the years come and that it will be far more economical for the city of Jacksonville at this time to acquire large areas for municipal parking than it will be to attempt to widen the streets of the city of Jacksonville. That municipal parking areas can be made self-sustaining by making a nominal charge for their use and in time to come will be a source of municipal revenue.

J. Parking Meters:

(Being of such controversial nature that no committee study was given. However, it is noted that it is only an adoption of the municipal parking area idea which uses the city streets as the site for charging a fee for parking in a preferred area.)

K. Traffic Engineer:

(It is the majority opinion of this committee that no "outside" technical employment be obtained or hired. That City Engineer W. E. Sheddan, County Engineer Arthur N. Sollee, Lieut. Reynolds, police department, are fully conversant with the problem after many years of study. That by cooperation of the elective officials of the city and county in above program, if carried out, will materially aid the present emergency and the future. That in the event employment of an engineer be required or desired, that serious consideration be given to securing George Simons, city planner.

L. Special Traffic Committee:

1. That the city council appoint and invite this committee to continue in office for a term of one year. That any member not being able to serve be replaced by substitute or new appointees.

2. That the city council provide the sum of $250 to meet the annual expenses of the committee.

3. That each member of the committee serve without compensation.

This report was the first evidence that a faint glow had begun to emerge from behind the clouds of timidity and uncertainty, and an awakening citizenry was beginning to grasp the economic value of excellent highways.

But with the great war raging, the possibilities of any type of construction, other than for pure military purposes, were put aside.

The Post War Era

Hardly had the last gun been fired, when from every section of America there came a crescendo of demands for an immediate program to improve the nation's highways. The enormous value of limited access expressways had been vividly demonstrated by the German Autobahns which were used so effectively to transport troops and war material from one region to another. Some say this system of high speed arterial highways connecting the principal German cities so impressed American highway engineers and military men that the United States counterpart was born and defined in the Federal Highway Act of 1944 as the "interregional interstate highway system."

A letter of June 5, 1945 from F. Elgin Bayless, chairman, Florida State Road Department, Tallahassee, Florida, to the chairmen, Boards of County Commissioners of Florida, stated: "The State Road Department planned to lay out a federal aid secondary system of highways which would act as feeder roads to the main state and federal aid system and requested each county to submit a list of approximately 100 miles of roads that should be placed on federal aid secondary."

This action by the state was instrumental in focusing the attention of the public in each county on the inadequacy of its roads, with the result that highway improvement committees were formed in the more progressive cities and counties in the state.

One June 11, 1945 a large group of citizens, representing many civic organizations from various sections of Florida, met in Tallahassee and adopted the following resolution:

WHEREAS the president of the United States did appoint a committee for the purpose of studying the post war highway needs of the country;

AND WHEREAS the committee did submit a plan for the construction of an integrated system of highways defined as the inter-regional highway system;

AND WHEREAS the Congress of the United States did incorporate this plan in the Federal Highway Act of 1944 and did therein cause the plan to be known as the interstate highway system;

AND WHEREAS the Seventy-eighth Congress of the United States has enacted a certain bill known as the Federal Highway Act of 1944 and has appropriated one billion five hundred millions of dollars for the financing of the act, said appropriation to be allocated to the several states and/or territories under the provisions of the act;

AND WHEREAS the several states and/or territories, to be eligible for participation under the act, are required by the provisions of the act, to match the funds appropriated under the federal act;

AND WHEREAS the several states and/or territories are required to submit to the Public Roads Administration of the Federal Works Agency, their proposed plans for participation under the act;

AND WHEREAS the Public Roads Administration of the Federal Works Agency has issued a regulation calling for the several states and/or territories to submit a tentative program of routes by July 1, 1944;

AND WHEREAS the express wording of the act is that the national system of interstate highways shall connect "as direct as practicable, the principal metropolitan areas, cities and industrial centers, to serve the national defense and to connect at suitable border points with routes of continental importance."

AND WHEREAS the interstate highway system plan recommends the following routes in Florida as being of prime necessity:

1. State Road No. 1 from Alabama State Line to Jacksonville;

2. State Road No. 2 from Georgia State Line to Lake City connecting with State Road No. 1 at Lake City.

3. State Road No. 3 from the Georgia State Line to Jacksonville.

4. State Road No. 4 from the Georgia State Line to Miami via Jacksonville, Daytona Beach, West Palm Beach to Miami.

5. State Road No. 21 from Daytona Beach to Deland.

6. State Road No. 2 and No. 17, from DeLand through Sanford, Orlando, Haines City to Tampa.

AND WHEREAS there exists a pressing need for the immediate construction of a north-south arterial highway as set forth in the interstate highway system plan;

NOW THEREFORE BE IT RESOLVED:

That this body acting severally and jointly as citizens and taxpayers of the state of Florida, and as accredited representatives of the several organizations present, does hereby request the State Road Department of Florida, at its regular session in Tallahassee, Florida, this the 11th day of June 1945, to immediately endorse to the Public Roads Administration of the Federal Works Agency the above described routes, as part of the interstate highway system, as being of the most urgent priority and certifying said routes for inclusion in the interim program in order to effectively utilize for the state of Florida the interim appropriation for planning, engineering and acquisition of right-of-ways.

BE IT FURTHER RESOLVED THAT:

This body, acting jointly and severally as citizens and as accredited representatives of the several organizations present, do hereby offer our full cooperation and assistance toward a successful conclusion of this program for a full and complete utilization of Florida's allocated share of the funds appropriated under the Federal Highway Act of 1944.

BE IT FURTHER RESOLVED that the original of this resolution be delivered to the State Road Department, in session, through its Chairman, the Hon. F. Elgin Bayless.

Signed _____
            Temporary Chairman

Attest _____
            Temporary Secretary

Done at Tallahassee, Florida, this 11th day of June in the year of our Lord Nineteen Hundred and Forty-five.

       Signature   Organization   Location

The County Commission of Duval County, W. Howard Belote, Robert D. Gordon, Tom Marshall, C. Ray Greene and Joe F. Hammond already had begun to formulate plans for post-war projects. On Tuesday, August 21, 1945 they instructed me as their county engineer to prepare and file with the Federal Works Agency, applications for an advance of federal funds to permit the preparation of plans and specifications for a bridge across the St. Johns River in the vicinity of Arlington and a system of countywide highways and drainage improvements.

Applications were filed but the county never received any federal funds as the processing was bogged down in the Washington bureaucratic red tape.

Undaunted by the lack of federal interest the commissioners began to work directly with S. Kendrick Guernsey, a member of the State Road Board who also was a citizen of Duval County. The county's suggested route for a highway skirting the northerly and westerly city limits of Jacksonville was presented to the Road Department and Guernsey advised the commissioners that he and the division engineer, John R. Slade, were in agreement that the proposed route was logical and needed, and that he was hopeful it would be included in the state's final plans. Guernsey had written to the chairman of the State Road Department that "Jacksonville and Duval County should not be deprived of this connecting link which is so badly needed now and should not have to wait several years for the construction of a route farther west." He maintained "the Cassat-Edgewood route could be constructed immediately with a minimum of cost and would continue to service traffic for another 10 to 20 years."

Unfortunately the State Highway Engineer Ham Dowling did not favor the beltway proposal and so again the people of Duval county were deprived of a much needed road facility.

The Year of 1946

The year of 1946 should go down as a memorable one in the long list of accomplishments by the Jacksonville Chamber of Commerce. A new highway committee was appointed by its chairman, Brown L. Whatley, to carry out a far-reaching, ambitious planning and construction program. The committee set its sights on the following six-point program made public in the *Jacksonville Journal* on February 19, 1946.

"1. To work closely with the Duval County Commission and the county engineer in the development of secondary roads.

"2. To exert every effort to insure the early completion of Hogan Road.

"3. To attempt to coordinate a master overall plan for the development of arterial highways and through routes which have a bearing on the traffic situation in the city of Jacksonville.

"4. To further activity for construction of a direct route from Jacksonville to Valdosta, Georgia.

"5. To press for construction of a connecting link between the south end of the Main Street Bridge and Phillips Highway to eliminate bottleneck at the south end of the bridge.

"6. To make a thorough study and analysis in the matter of constructing and financing an additional bridge across the St. Johns River in the Arlington area."

It was most fortunate at this time that the representative of the second district of the State Road Department was S. Kendrick Guernsey, a most able man and a resident of Duval County, for by working with Mr. Guernsey, the Highway Committee had a direct line of communication with the department. It was due to the untiring zeal of Mr. Guernsey and the pleas of Brown L. Whatley as chairman of the Highway Committee, that the state made a comprehensive traffic study of the highway needs of Duval County.

On Tuesday, July 16, 1946 in the Seminole Hotel, at a luncheon meeting of the Highway Committee of the Jacksonville Chamber of Commerce, W. M. Parker, an engineer with the research and records division of the State Road Department outlined the route of a proposed $16,345,000 superhighway through Jacksonville. He explained the plan was merely an engineering analysis of the actual traffic situation in Jacksonville with a recommended solution. Committee chairman Brown L. Whatley said he would appoint a representative committee of Jacksonville leaders to study the plan. Local leaders at the luncheon represented the City Commission and Council, County Commission, Traffic Advisory Committee, Citizens' Steering Committee and City Planning and Advisory Board.

Within one week, Whatley announced the Interstate Highway Committee, a subsidiary of the Jacksonville Chamber of Commerce's Highway Committee, would study the proposed route of the superhighway through Jacksonville. Those named to serve on this committee were James R. Stockton, L. A. Raulerson, White L. Moss, Robert M. Angas, Sgt. J. H. Allen, Maynard Burrell, George W. Gibbs, Sr., T. C. Imeson, Tom Marshall, John E. Mathews, Robert R. Milam, Allen Poucher, Ralph H. Spaulding, J. P. Walker, Frank W. Sherman and Harold W. Whitehead.

The *Jacksonville Journal* also stepped into the picture with an editorial in their Wednesday, July 17, 1946 edition:

"With the presentation yesterday of the State Road Department's plan for solving Jacksonville's traffic difficulties, all possible reason for delay in action has been put behind us. Now, to the various plans advanced by Jaxons themselves during recent years, has been added one formulated by state engineers after a traffic survey which consumed more than a year.

"The thing now is for all of the agencies involved — city, county, state and federal to get together for the next step — for action. The time for mere talk and for 'plans' is now past. Let us now raise funds, acquire the necessary rights of way, and start work on the roads, tunnels, bridges, overpasses or whatever is necessary to get Jacksonville out of the hard traffic knot into which it has been tied during its recent period of rapid growth. There has been no shortage of talk, of committees, of surveys, or private projects and pet plans. Let us call a halt on these now and get into constructive action.

"What's the next step? The city and county should lose no time to decide what they want and can do — and get to work."

The paper also came out with a twelve point platform for Jacksonville which called for "completion of the Cross-Florida Barge Canal, a recreation center, stadium and auditorium, a beautiful river front with drives, a tunnel or third bridge across the St. Johns, a housing and slum clearance program, four year college, a state medical school, an adequate number of city buses, expansion of both municipal airports, an expanded light plant, more street lights, a city water softening plant and a scientific traffic survey and plan."

During the ensuing months numerous mass meetings were held in the Springfield area, on the Southside and in the Arlington section of the county. In presenting the superhighway plans, Mr. Whatley went to much pains to explain that the plans under discussion were merely tentative, submitted by the state engineers after months of research and had not been endorsed by anybody. It was stressed that the issue was a national one and not a local issue. In presentations by Edward Hobbs, the industrial secretary for the Chamber of Commerce, he emphasized the fact that the highway proposal was part of an interstate program.

A torrent of discussion followed every citizens meeting, it being unanimous that two more bridges across the St. Johns River were needed, not just the one proposed by the state and federal government.

In addition to the numerous civic groups pushing for the construction of a major arterial highway through the city were other satellite groups. Their voices could be heard at every open mass meeting. In committee meetings their spokesmen were very articulate in endeavoring to "change" the alignment or the location of a bridge so that traffic would go by their businesses. Subtle efforts were even made to have the highway go through certain areas in order that the property would have to be acquired for right of way purposes.

Fortunately, the established alignment for the various segments of the highway, the results of engineering studies and requirements, were adhered to within reasonable variations.

While the State Road Department considered the possibility of including a low level bridge to Arlington in their plans, the County Commission continued to insist on the need for a high level bridge across the St. Johns River with connections to Atlantic Boulevard and to Phillips Highway, in the vicinity of Greenland. The commission had instructed me to prepare a prospectus covering their ideas as well as the thinking of the informed citizens of the entire county. This report was presented to the commission at a regular meeting held on Tuesday morning October 8, 1946. The *Jacksonville Journal* the same afternoon gave complete coverage of the engineer's report and the news story as publicized is now quoted in part.

> Plans for a high-level bridge connecting East Jacksonville and Arlington which are being placed before the Board of County Commissioners today have been evolved not only with a view to the efficient handling of expected peacetime traffic, but also from the standpoint of fast and efficient Army and Navy movement in case of war, County Engineer Arthur N. Sollee said this morning.
>
> Sollee and County Commissioner Joe Hammond, who has long been a champion of the Arlington span, reviewed the bridge specifications in the courthouse prior to formal presentation to the board. After receiving official approval, the data will be forwarded to the citizens' committee now studying such projects in connection with a proposed bond issue.

"Span Proposed in 1929"

Plans for an Arlington bridge have been before the county board off and on since 1929, Sollee said, and while changes and modifications have been made since that time there has been no deviation from the principle that it must be a high-level span with sufficient clearance for any vessel.

Another important factor emphasizing the need of a high-level bridge, Hammond pointed out, is the possibility of practically all the intracoastal waterway traffic being diverted from its present route through the St. Johns River in front of Jacksonville, thence on to Sanford, thence by way of a new canal to the Indian River near Titusville.

Asked why the county board preferred the high-level bridge to the tunnel that has also been suggested, Sollee said that the most important objection to the tunnel was its cost. Studies of both bridges and tunnel construction throughout the country show that it is much more expensive, per traffic lane, to go under the water. Then too, it costs more to maintain a tunnel than a bridge and in some instances it has been found necessary to deny the use of tunnels to some types of vehicles such as gasoline trucks.

"Beauty Enters In"

But Sollee and Hammond were both agreed that even with costs and other practical considerations the same, they would still prefer the bridge. Their reasons for this were aesthetic.

"We like people to see the St. Johns River," they said, "because it's a beautiful sight. We don't want them to burrow under it."

"Bridge Aids Defense"

The engineer claimed that the proposed bridge fits perfectly into the scheme of national defense by providing a sure and definite link between the east coast of Florida and the north.

"A minimum of expense is of course highly desirable, but the road or bridge which is truly cheapest is not the one which has cost the least amount of money. It is the one that makes the most profitable return in proportion to the amount spent on it," Sollee asserted. "The trend in Duval County is now to the south and east, and it is not inconceivable that in the not too distant future all of the area between Jacksonville and the ocean will be built up solidly. The Arlington bridge would be the logical route to and from the Beaches for traffic originating north of and adjacent to Beaver Street, and as such would relieve the Main Street and St. Johns River bridges of much traffic."

Many conferences held during November and December were attended by local highway committee groups and representatives of the State Road Department, to coordinate the thinking and ideas into a highway plan acceptable by all.

Finally, on Friday, December 27, 1946 at a luncheon meeting in the Seminole Hotel W. M. Parker, Division Engineer of Research and Records, State Road Department, announced that Jacksonville's segment of the nationwide interstate highway had been approved by the Federal Bureau of Public Roads. He also said the State Road Department had adopted all of the suggestions made by the special highway committee which included the high-level Arlington Bridge and approach roads.

Mr. Whatley announced the approximate cost of the entire project was $36,000,000 with a self-liquidating bond to cover local financing of the program. The revenue from toll collections on the three bridges would be used solely for the retirement of the bonds.

County Road and Bridge Projects - 1930's

Love Grove Road, now University Blvd. N. Looking South from Chaseville Rd. April 29, 1936

Love Grove Road, now University Blvd. South Looking South from Hogan Road, now Beach Blvd. April 13, 1936

Love Grove Road - Now University Blvd. West Looking South from Atlantic Blvd. S.R. No. 78 July 15, 1936

CHAPTER IX

The Year of 1947

Another forward step was taken in January for the planning of the proposed $36,000,000 inter-regional highway, the Arlington Bridge and Approaches project, when the State Road Department appointed F. Elgin Bayless, its chairman, to work with the State Improvement Commission. Bayless was selected upon motion of S. Kendrick Guernsey, board member from Jacksonville.

Things seemed to be going along peacefully until Commission Director C. H. Overman of The Florida State Improvement Commission announced that the commission would require tolls on the existing Acosta and Alsop St. Johns River bridges in Jacksonville, if it financed construction of three additional spans in the proposed $36,000,000 highway project. These spans would be one across Trout River, another across the St. Johns River from the Riverside area to South Jacksonville and the third from downtown Jacksonville easterly to the community of Arlington. He said, however, the board would consider financing a $22,000,000 development — without construction of a new bridge at Arlington and without tolls on the Acosta and Alsop bridges, if the county would pledge part of its gasoline tax surplus to help pay the debt. Tolls would be charged only on the new bridges under this plan.

A tornado passing through the heart of Jacksonville could not have stirred up the local citizens and the county commissioners any more than this pronouncement from Tallahassee by the Improvement Commission. Tempers flared, telephone calls were made and wires were sent protesting the apparent dictatorial attitude of the Tallahassee body.

After a series of verbal barrages, the county commission on March 27th unanimously adopted a resolution to construct the super highway system and the Arlington Bridge project. The resolution included a pledge of 80 percent of surplus gasoline taxes allocated to the State Road Department for use within the county. Copies of the resolution were forwarded to Governor Millard F. Caldwell as chairman of the State Improvement Commission.

On August 6th the S.I.C. received a preliminary report from its financial adviser, Welsh, Davis Banking Company of Chicago that the Arlington Bridge would lower the price of bonds and increase the interest rates for the rest of the project. H. H. Baskin, a member of the commission from Clearwater, said the commission was jeopardizing the entire Jacksonville interstate project just to meet the demands for the Arlington span.

This latest bombshell came just as the citizens of Jacksonville were preening themselves with satisfaction that every objection to the Arlington Bridge as part of the superhighway project had been overcome.

The reaction of the County Commission on learning of the bid to financially scuttle the Arlington Bridge was a unanimous Arlington Bridge or nothing. The commissioners' attitude that the interests of the local citizens must be considered if the county was to tie up its gasoline tax moneys, was backed by Senator John E. Mathews.

The firm stand taken by Duval County resulted in the S.I.C. deciding to appear before the County Commission to amplify their version of the problem. A two-hour public meeting was held in the courthouse on Monday, August 18th where the S.I.C.'s views were presented by F. Elgin Bayless.

He warned the County Commissioners and other interested parties that all or a major part of future gasoline tax revenues quite possibly would be required in liquidating the project. He reiterated an earlier pledge of the State Road Department that "this entire $36,000,000 project will be completed." He declared, "State and federal funds will be utilized in building feeder and auxiliary roads to round out the superhighway and Duval County will be called upon to guarantee the repayment of approximately $22,000,000, representing the revenue certificates."

Brown Whatley stated: "I am firmly convinced the future destiny of Jacksonville and all of Duval County is at stake today. I say, let's go ahead with this entire plan which is essential to our future growth and expansion." He presented the group a resolution adopted Friday, August 15th by the Board of Governors of the Jacksonville Chamber of Commerce wherein the Board of County Commissioners was urged to restate its position that surplus gasoline tax as may be necessary be committed to guarantee the entire project.

Acting in good faith, the County Commission the following week authorized the Pittsburgh Testing Laboratory to proceed immediately with borings for pier construction as an initial step in building the Arlington span.

On Tuesday, October 8th the State Improvement Commission empowered Elgin Bayless, chairman of the State Road Department, to employ consulting engineers to prepare a traffic survey of Duval County to show the financial soundness of the proposed $36,000,000 superhighway system. The commission also asked the road department to consider drawing plans for the proposed Arlington span and that a consulting engineer be called in to assist the department and engineers in this work.

Once again peace and quiet prevailed in Duval County for at last, so it seemed, all points of conflict had been ironed out.

The Year of 1948

Crews of men worked in two shifts on traffic origin and destination surveys through the winter of 1947-48, to be used in evaluating the possible earnings of the toll bridges planned for inclusion in the superhighway project. Reports indicated that the general public cooperated to the fullest extent with the checkers.

The first indication the engineering report had been completed came from the Board of County Commissioners on June 15th when the board voted to advise the public that the Coverdale and Colpitts report had been received, and was under consideration. Copies were on file in the county engineer's office for public inspection.

Commissioner Tom Marshall declared, "It will be the board's intention at some future date to call a public hearing for a full discussion of the entire question."

The report established a cost of the basic system at $22,500,000. It explained this did not include the construction of feeder and lateral highways, which would be built over a period of years and financed by joint state and federal contributions estimated to cost another $12,000,000.

A warm controversy started between Elgin Bayless, State Road Department chairman and County Commissioner Marshall when Marshall said, "For one thing, the financing arrangements seem to have changed since the highway plan was originally approved by the county commission." Bayless countered by stating, "There is nothing in the financing plan about using up all Duval County surplus gas taxes to pay off the cost of this project. They are pledged only to make up any possible deficiency in bridge tolls."

The public did not realize that this exchange of words hid the seething tempers of the county officials, who felt the new proposals by both branches of the state government were at considerable variance with the original plan that had been approved on March 26, 1947. Therefore, at their meeting on Tuesday, June 29th the commissioners voted unanimously to rescind their approval of the proposed $34,500,000 superhighway plan and directed that Coverdale and Colpitts' report be referred to the county engineer for detailed study and analysis, and that he report his findings and recommendations to the board at the earliest practicable date.

A tropical hurricane could not have brought more consternation to some of the local backers of the state's plan than the pronouncement of the county. Almost instantaneously the commissioners were swamped by threats of some local groups to go ahead with the plans. One state official, C. H. Overman, Director of the S.I.C. suggested Duval County be ignored and Jacksonville bypassed. State Road Chairman, F. Elgin Bayless was quoted as saying, "Let's either get it or forget it." Bayless said in a statement made in Tallahassee that his agency "has gone on record on several occasions that it would undertake construction of these neccesary connections as state and federal funds become available—probably over the next 10 years."

Commissioner Marshall declared that the board must look at the proposal from a business and not a political point of view.

Senator John E. Mathews stated he believed "that the Board of County Commissioners had acted wisely in asking for a detailed analysis of the reports by their engineer and in giving all interested citizens an opportunity to study this question before final action is taken."

The cannonading continued with intermittent shots being fired through news items from Tallahassee and Duval County. It seemed that every time an official of the State Road Department or Improvement Commission gave out a statement he, figuratively speaking, "put his foot in it." As an example, I quote from the Wednesday, July 14, 1948 *Jacksonville Journal*:

> "State officials maintain there has been no change in the plan, and Bayless has said the Road Department has repeatedly said it would construct the feeder roads as money becomes available over the next 10 years. H. H. Basken, Clearwater, member of the Improvement Commission, suggested if Duval County doesn't want to participate in the project the state might consider an interregional highway by bypassing Jacksonville. 'We'll never bypass Jacksonville,' Bayless replied. 'The problem there is local traffic. It's something they need for their own economic growth.' "

Duval County commissioners asserted plans for the bridges were "far from dead despite the shelving of the superhighway project by the State Improvement Commission." They directed the county engineer to continue his study of the proposal and to bring back to the county board "not just criticisms of that plan, but concrete recommendations to integrate its basic conceptions into our county's actual traffic needs." Commissioner Marshall pointed out the state's plan "didn't give Duval County a thing — we were burying everything in it with our gasoline tax revenue and with tolls collected right here." He said when the local board completes its report on "any superhighway plan," and if it is submitted to any state board or agency for consideration, "we won't demand that we get a final yes or no answer within 60 days, a requirement that State Improvement Commission and the State Road Department apparently imposed on Duval County."

With these final statements from all political bodies the issue subsided into the sleep of a smoldering volcano.

CHAPTER XI
The Year of 1949

The 1945-1948 administration of Governor Millard Caldwell had come to an inglorious end as far as Duval Countians were concerned. New faces appeared on the political horizon, and appointees fresh from their business activities in private life were spokesmen for newly elected officials.

Such was the stage in 1949. Fuller Warren began his term of office as Florida's governor in January and the members of his official family began to familiarize themselves with the myriad of state problems. And with the governor from Duval County, new hopes were raised in the hearts of the local citizens that at last the county's problems would be received with friendly ears. Too, J. Glover Taylor, a Jacksonville resident, was appointed as a member of the State Road Board. So why should not the people of Duval County look forward to the next four years with smiles?

The pent-up desires of the community for traffic relief, dormant for several months, burst forth with renewed vigor in early spring. An announcement was made by the County Commission on Wednesday, March 9th that the board would meet with the State Road Board and the Florida Improvement Commission in Tallahassee the following Tuesday, to discuss the county's proposed method of financing. The *Jacksonville Journal* aptly depicted the thinking of all Duval Countians in its Monday, March 14th edition with the cartoon reproduced at right.

Am I Seeing Things?

The conference in Tallahassee on Tuesday, March 15th should be marked on the calendar of historic events for Duval County as the real beginning of positive action in the long struggle to construct an expressway system in Duval County.

A revised superhighway project was presented to the state group by Senator John E. Mathews, acting as spokesman for the delegation of Duval County and Jacksonville officials. The new plan approved differed from the long-discussed superhighway in many essential particulars. It gave the state board a timetable of "first needs met first," emphasizing the urgency of immediate construction of two new St. Johns River bridges and the simultaneous opening of traffic-expediting arteries to the new spans as well as the existing ones. Acceptance of it was moved by Governor Fuller Warren, ex-officio member of the Improvement Commission, and seconded by Alfred A. McKethan, chairman of the State Road Board.

The Improvement Commission adopted a resolution which called for the County Commission of Duval County to adopt an appropriate resolution to meet the legal requirements for the issuance of bonds contemplated for the program. It also requested the State Road Department to prepare necessary plans and specifications for the improvements "as early as practical." It further directed that as soon as engineering and financing details were completed that construction be started immediately.

The Duval County delegation appearing before the Improvement Commission included C. Ray Greene, chairman; Tom Marshall, Robert D. Gordon, Joe F. Hammond and Edward I. Acosta of the County Commission; J. Henry Blount, county attorney; Arthur N. Sollee, county engineer; Senator Mathews and Representatives Charles A. Luckie, Mabry Carlton and Fletcher Morgan; C. Frank Whitehead, mayor of Jacksonville; William Sheddan, city engineer and Walter G. Daniels, assistant city engineer; Harry Howard Jr., city traffic engineer; Earle E. Jones, secretary of the Jacksonville City Commission; Robert C. Lechner, member of the Duval County Board of Public Instruction; former State Senator J. Turner Butler; J. Glover Taylor, Jacksonville member of the State Road Department; Cleveland Johnson and Carl D. Langston, representing the Arlington Community Club.

Members of the delegation were asked by Improvement Commission Chairman Dodge Taylor to discuss the new proposal. It was unanimously endorsed by the speakers.

Answering questions from Governor Warren and Chairman McKethan covering the location and financial feasibility of the proposed highway and bridge project, Senator Mathews declared the proposal was statewide in its scope and would be the "most important undertaking in the state of Florida."

J. Glover Taylor commented that the project was vitally needed "to alleviate an intolerable traffic situation." The county's representatives, Luckie, Carlton and Morgan declared they were "all working together to see this project materialize and endorse it wholeheartedly."

Former Senator J. Turner Butler said estimates of revenues and the retirement plan for bonds were ultraconservative.

The county engineer pointed out the basic differences between the current proposal and the original superhighway project developed more than a year ago by members of the former State Road Department.

The other proposal, he said, obligated Duval County in the amount of about $22,500,000 and carried with it an "indefinite" promise of state aid amounting to about $12,000,000.

The state's contribution, he declared, would have provided one north-south traffic artery from the main Street road, over a new bridge at Trout River, over the Myrtle Avenue overpass and across the St. Johns River via the Riverside-Southside Bridge. It also provided for the Arlington Bridge. However, no provisions were made for access arteries to the Arlington span and nothing was contemplated that would have immediately relieved the bottlenecks at the southern approach to the existing bridges.

The state's contribution, in the original plan, would have provided access to the main north-south artery from highways leading into Jacksonville from the north, south and west, but the proposal gave no concrete timetable for that construction. No provision was made in the original project for the acquisition of rights of way for the state portion of the road construction which would involve costs of about $1,500,000, the engineer pointed out.

"We have substituted a workable four-year program designed to end our major traffic problems for an unwieldy project which could not have been completed in under 10 years," the county engineer said. "We have reduced the county's prospective indebtedness by about $4,000,000 and outlined a state contribution which is within the bounds of reason. We have, we believe, drafted a plan which meets our county's major needs and conforms to the wishes of a majority of our citizens."

The Tuesday conference was a remarkable demonstration of accomplishment and proved that men with a common goal were capable of unanimous action. And, each political entity completed its particular function so that all of the commissioners and boards approved on all required resolutions in the following chronological order:

Tuesday, March 15th Tallahassee, Florida, Approval of resolution by the Florida State Improvement Commission:

WHEREAS, The Board of County Commissioners of Duval County, Florida, have submitted a proposal for the construction of the improvements in Duval County known as the Arlington Bridge -St. Johns River (Riverside) Bridge as a portion of the interstate highway, the particulars being set forth in detail in a report by Arthur N. Sollee, county engineer of Duval County, dated December 1, 1948, which was submitted with the proposal of the Board of County Commissioners; and

WHEREAS, said proposal contemplates the issuance of $19,000,000 of certificates of indebtedness, and the tolls of said two bridges to be fixed and determined by the Florida State Improvement Commission and State Road Department; and also 80 percent of the surplus gasoline tax accruing to the State Road Department for

Duval County, pursuant to the provisions of Article 9, Section 16, of the Constitution of Florida, be pledged through the instrumentality of the Florida State Improvement Commission as security for the payment of said certificates of indebtedness; and

WHEREAS it appears that the proposal submitted by the Board of County Commissioners is feasible, and the sum of $19,000,000 will be sufficient to construct the Arlington Bridge and the St. Johns River (Riverside) Bridge and the immediate approaches thereto, and provide necessary engineering costs in connection therewith, and will also be sufficient to pay the cost of rights of way for the entire project:

NOW THEREFORE BE IT RESOLVED by the Florida State Improvement Commission that the entire proposal be undertaken as early as practical, and that the following steps be taken:

1. The Board of County Commissioners of Duval County adopt the required resolution to meet legal requirements for the issuance of bonds or certificates of indebtedness herein contemplated.

2. That in order to expedite the matter the Road Department be requested to have prepared as early as practical plans and specifications for the contemplated improvements.

3. As soon as the financing and engineering can be completed, that there be immediately undertaken (a) the construction of the Arlington Bridge and the necessary roads and approaches in connection therewith, as outlined in the proposal submitted by the Board of County Commissioners; and (b) the construction of the St. Johns River (Riverside) Bridge and the immediate approaches thereto.

4. That the remainder of the program, including the Trout River Bridge, be constructed by the State Road Department as and when the funds are available from regular sources of income of the State Road Department, including federal aid, which would naturally be allocated to Duval County in the future years.

Monday, March 28th — Vero Beach, Florida. Approval of resolution by State Road Department.

WHEREAS on March 15, 1949 the Florida State Improvement Commission adopted a resolution approving a proposal submitted by the Board of County Commissioners in and for Duval County, Florida, with reference to the construction and financing of improvements in Duval County known as the Arlington Bridge - St. Johns River (Riverside) Bridge as a portion of the interstate highway, the particulars being set forth in detail in a report submitted by Arthur N. Sollee, county engineer of Duval County, dated December 1, 1948, which was submitted with the proposal of the Board of County Commissioners; and

WHEREAS a copy of said resolution has been filed with this board, and in and by said resolution this board was requested to have prepared as early as possible plans and specifications for the contemplated improvements, in order that the actual construction of said improvements may be expedited; and

WHEREAS the resolution adopted by the Florida State Improvement Commission contemplates that the improvements will be constructed under agreements or contracts to be entered into by this board and the Florida State Improvement Commission, in cooperation with the Board of Administration; and

WHEREAS the proposal submitted by the Board of County Commissioners of Duval County, and the resolution adopted by the Florida State Improvement Commission, contemplate that funds for the construction of the proposed bridges and the approaches thereto will be obtained by the Florida State Improvement Commission by the issuance and sale of revenue bonds in the principal sum of $19,000,000, to be paid out of the proceeds of a lease-purchase agreement with the State Road Department, the rentals under which are to be paid by the State Road Department from tolls on the two bridges and from 80 percent surplus gasoline tax funds of Duval County derived from the 2 cents gasoline tax imposed under Section 16, Article 9 of the Constitution of the state of Florida; and further that the legal and fiscal sufficiency of the proceedings authorizing the issuance of said bonds shall be approved by the State Board of Administration:

NOW THEREFORE BE IT RESOLVED by the State Road Department of the state of Florida that this board concur in and approve the resolution adopted by the Florida State Improvement Commission on March 15, 1949.

BE IT FURTHER RESOLVED that the chairman and attorney for this board be and they are hereby authorized and directed to confer and negotiate with the chairman and attorney for the Florida State Improvement Commission and the chairman and attorney for the Board of Administration with reference to the contracts and agreements to be entered into and the resolution or resolutions to be adopted by the Board of County Commissioners in and for Duval

County, and that as soon as said resolutions have been prepared and shall meet with the approval of the chairman and attorneys for the respective departments, that the same be submitted to the Board of County Commissioners of Duval County, with the request that such resolution or resolutions be adopted.

BE IT FURTHER RESOLVED that the chairman and attorney of this board be and they are hereby authorized and directed to take all needful steps to carry out the full purpose and intent of this resolution, and of the resolution adopted by the Florida State Improvement Commission on March 15, 1949.

Adopted by State Road Department at their regular meeting, held at Vero Beach, Florida, March 28, 1949.

Tuesday, April 26th a special sub-committee of the Chamber of Commerce was appointed by chairman Brown L. Whatley to assist the county engineer in certain details of routing and priority in construction of the superhighway and bridge project for Duval County.

Monday, May 2nd a meeting was held by the Chamber of Commerce Highway subcommittee to discuss the proposed expressway. Committee members present were: Brown Whatley, Ed Hobbs, L. A. Raulerson, Roland Meyer, S. L. Monroe, William Johnson and Robert Angas. Visitors were Charles Johnson, Al Bolsch and Arthur Newkirk. The county engineer was also present.

The meeting turned out to be an attempt by the "visitors" to "ram" through a "priority plan of work for the expressway." Charles Johnson presented his plan which would suit the motel operators on Philips Highway but to the detriment of the overall plan.

July 12th: The Chamber of Commerce Highway Committee unanimously adopted a priority plan for constructing the various segments of the superhighway and bridge project based upon its subcommittee recommendation drafted after conferences with the county commissioners and county engineer.

Sunday, September 25th: Origin and destination surveys were started in order to determine the travel habits of the local motorists.

Wednesday, October 5th: The Southside Business Men's Club adopted a super-highway priority list in sharp conflict with the one approved by the county commission. Arthur Newkirk, the club's chairman of its highway committee, said "our plan would move traffic through Jacksonville expeditiously and protect our property."

The Southside club voiced opposition to one-way street systems in their part of the city unless all other measures to relieve traffic jams fail.

The club asked for further study of the traffic problem at Times Square, including the possibility of building a traffic circle there.

Thursday, October 6th: Chairman Alfred A. McKethan, State Road Department, announced that he had received reports of the consulting engineers, Reynolds, Smith and Hills of Jacksonville and Parsons, Brinckerhoff, Hall and MacDonald of New York concerning the two proposed new bridges across the St. Johns River and the Myrtle Avenue overpass. He said, "It is the Road Department's plan to do this job all as one, and not a piece at a time. The entire program is a joint county, state and federal aid project."

Friday, December 2nd: The county commission meeting in special session unanimously adopted a resolution endorsing a plan for financing the superhighway project, to cost an estimated $41,818,000 and authorizing the Florida Improvement Commission to issue revenue bonds for $28,000,000 of that cost.

The proposal was presented to the board by Alfred A. McKethan. He explained that the plan contemplates the use of $13,818,000 of state and federal funds, in addition to the $28,000,000 to be provided by the revenue certificates. He declared, "right of way agents and survey engineers will be buzzing around in your midst in a matter of days. I am sure you are aware that the road board has only three more years to serve in its present capacity. We all have the philosophy of not starting anything we cannot finish and therefore you may be assured we will exert every effort humanly possible to finish this project during the remaining three years of Governor Warren's administration."

Wednesday, December 14th: McKethan announced that the "last hurdle" in the way of Duval County's $42,000,000 express highway project had been cleared with unqualified endorsement by the Federal Bureau of Public Roads.

Monday, December 19th: No protests were registered at a public hearing held by the U.S. Army Engineers for the construction of the Gilmore Street Bridge and the high level span to Arlington across the St. Johns River.

County Road and Bridge Projects - 1930's

Beach Boulevard as it appeared on July 14, 1939 - looking east from Big Pottsburg Creek

Beach Boulevard as it appeared on July 14, 1939 - removing muck by hand with W.P.A. labor

Typical Windrow - Barber-Greene Mixing Plant in background 1939

CHAPTER XII
The Year of 1950

Thursday, January 12th: The State Road Department offered the County Commission informal but strong assurances that its full proposed program of improvements and construction of 23 primary and secondary roads would be included in the department's 1950 budget.

Chairman McKethan and members of the Road Board pledged the county's program would be carried out in full during 1950.

This was the program:

Construction to be undertaken with regular funds of the State Road Department included the Ribault River Bridge on Lem Turner Road, the Valdosta-Jacksonville short cut, the improvement of Atlantic Boulevard from Barbara Street to Beach Boulevard, the Sisters Creek Bridge on Heckscher Drive, the widening and resurfacing of Atlantic Boulevard from Beach Boulevard to Third Street, Neptune Beach; the widening of Hendricks Avenue from San Marco Boulevard to Love Grove Road, the paving of S.R. 228 from Cassat Avenue to Normandy Boulevard, the construction of additional lanes on Phillips Highway from South Jacksonville to Bayard, the widening of S.R. 10 in the town of Baldwin and widening the same road westerly from Jacksonville to Baldwin.

The farm-to-market road improvement program included:

Eastport Road, from U.S. 17 to S.R. 105; Edgewood Avenue, from Lem Turner Road to Lenox Avenue; Cassat Avenue from Edgewood Avenue to Blanding Boulevard; Love Grove Road from Atlantic Boulevard to Hendricks Avenue; Duval Road from Main Street to Pecan Park Road; Avenue B, from Moncrief Road to the Jacksonville city limits; Garden Street, from Kings Road to Jones Road; Jones Road, from Garden Street to U.S. 90; Ricker Road, from Jacksonville Heights Road to Middleburg Road; Middleburg Road, from Ricker Road to Lenox Avenue; Sunbeam Road, from U.S. 1 to S.R. 13 and San Pablo Road from Atlantic Boulevard to Beach Boulevard.

The reader is urged to make a mental note of the foregoing list of road improvement and construction projects that were to be included in the State Road Department's budget for 1950.

Hardly had the State Road Department agreed to begin work on the $42,000,000 expressway, when loud protests were heard from City Engineer-Consultant W.E. Sheddan, the Jacksonville City Commission and spokesmen for the Baptist Hospital Board of Trustees, that the proposed southside location of the Gilmore Street Bridge at Gary Street should be moved to Nira Street.

The trustees claimed that the southside approach at Gary Street would materially damage their property for which they had paid $217,000. They declared that design and construction of the Baptist Hospital was stymied until it was learned how much hospital property along Gary Street would be required for construction of approaches to the Gilmore Street Bridge.

Senator John E. Mathews declared the disputed Gary Street approach would be of "tremendous benefit in the construction of the Baptist Memorial Hospital." He said, "I have contacted Alfred A. McKethan, of the State Road Department, and received his assurances of every cooperation with the hospital trustees so the bridge will not interfere in any way with the hospital construction, but actually will materially benefit it."

The problem was finally resolved after many conferences between representatives of the Florida State Road Department and Baptist Hospital trustees.

It would be foolish to say that efforts were not made to change certain basic features of the expressway plan and as an example I received from a friend in New York City the following excerpts from the *Tourist Court Journal* for February, 1950.

Charles M. Johnson, Johnson Manor Courts, Jacksonville, Florida. The 1948-49 season was our best year in business. This season 1949-50 so far portends to be about 10-15% off of last year—though this should show a decided upswing toward the end of December.

Jacksonville has been and is now quite a bottleneck for tourists on account of traffic conditions. However, we will shortly commence actual work on probably the largest construction project of improved highways in the Southeast. A $41,000,000 super-express highway system connecting all highways leading into Jacksonville bringing travelers through Jacksonville at 40-50 mph with plenty of access leads into the heart of the downtown area. There has been a lot of politics in it and, as usual, I have been personally in the middle of it to get the Southside angle of it when it would do the most good for the fine group of tourist courts we have here. It's been a real mess and a hard fight but thank goodness it's definitely and finally set now and will pass by our doors. This entire project will be connected within three years (during the present administration) and involves three new bridges, overpasses, etc. It means final sound property values for the courts in South Jacksonville and unquestionably will greatly enhance the property value of the courts over here. I firmly believe we are definitely in the "driver's seat" now, but it has been one big worry.

All of the news was good during the balance of 1950 and it was recorded in *The Florida Times-Union* as follows:

Wednesday, March 8th: Legal action by the Board of County Commissioners was authorized yesterday for the condemnation of state designated rights of way for Duval county's $42,000,000 superhighway.

Friday, March 10th: Arlington Bridge bids are sought. Half million dollars worth of work on piers marks first step in superhighway says Chairman McKethan of State Road Board.

Thursday, March 30th: State purchases first residence on superhighway. Transfer of former home of Dr. Frederick J. Waas at Gilmore and May streets made yesterday for bridge right of way.

Tuesday, April 11th: State Road Board holds second meeting in Duval County and the first bids were opened for constructing eight approach piers to the planned Arlington Bridge. The George D. Auchter Company was the apparent low bidder at $330,982.

Wednesday, May 17th: The first pile for the Arlington Bridge was driven into the ground at 11:38 A.M. yesterday at the foot of Hill Street.

Saturday, May 20th: The first gift of land needed in connection with the Jacksonville expressway was reported yesterday by E.F. Bellows, right of way expeditor for the State Road Department. Bellows said the needed parcel comprises a part of the easterly approach for the Arlington Bridge and the gift by Landon M. Lockwood and his wife, Mrs. Miriam Lockwood, "may inspire other owners of small parcels along the expressway route to convey them to the state as gifts."

Thursday, May 25th: The State Improvement Commission, yesterday in Tallahassee, authorized the sale of $28,000,000 of revenue bonds for the superhighway and bridge system in Jacksonville.

Tuesday, June 6th: The State Road Department yesterday approved a lease-purchase agreement with the State Improvement Commission for Jacksonville's $41,818,000 superhighway development program.

Wednesday, June 14th: The Board of County Commissioners formally ratified an earlier pledge that it would guarantee the repayment of a $28,000,000 Jacksonville expressway system bond issue by earmarking its 80 percent of surplus gasoline tax refunds to meet the principal and interest payments on the obligation.

J. Turner Butler, attorney for the improvement body, pointed out that in return for the pledge of gasoline tax income to retire the $28,000,000 bond issue, Duval County has been guaranteed an expenditure here of at least $41,800,000 including a $13,800,000 contribution from the State Road Department and the Federal Bureau of Roads.

Wednesday, July 25th: The final legal hurdle in the path of a $28,000,000 bond issue for the Jacksonville Expressway was cleared yesterday with record breaking speed when the proposed issue was validated by a unanimous decision of the Florida Supreme Court.

Wednesday, August 2nd: The State Road Department has advanced another $200,000 to speed the acquisition of right of way for the superhighway, J. Glover Taylor, local member of the Road Board announced yesterday, also adding that the grant, which must be repaid to the general fund when the $28,000,000 super-highway bond issue is sold, brings to about $1,300,000 the sum which has been made available for the project.

Tuesday, September 26th: Bond dealers today snapped up a $28,000,000 state issue to help finance the Jacksonville expressway.

A dealer syndicate headed by the New York firm of Smith, Barney and Company bought the bonds at an interest rate of 2.6— said authoritatively to be the lowest ever obtained anywhere for a project of this magnitude lacking a history of earning ability. The bonds were sold at competitive bidding by the State Improvement Commission, a financing vehicle for state agencies.

Senator Mathews, hailed at the meeting as a never-daunted leader of the development for more than two decades, was honored to the extent of the authority of the Improvement Commission through its naming the Arlington Bridge for him.

Responding to the reiterated urging that he permit the expressway to be named for him, Governor Warren said in part, "I must reject your fine proposal for I have a conscientious and deep-seated objection to public officials with the power to name bridges and other public works, using that power to memorialize themselves."

Thursday, October 5th: The State Road Department has chosen Lee Street for the northerly approach of the superhighway into the heart of the city, it was disclosed yesterday when right of way maps for the route between Imeson Airport and Eighteenth Street were released.

Both Lee and Davis Streets, which lie parallel a block apart, had been considered for the route. The final route was chosen because buildings along Lee Street are generally less valuable than those along Davis.

Monday, October 23rd: Governor Fuller Warren prepared in New York City today for the "significant milestone" chore of signing his name 1400 times on Jacksonville expressway bonds.

Former State Senator J. Turner Butler of Jacksonville, who has had the responsibility for bringing the expressway into reality as attorney for the Florida State Improvement Commission, said the formal delivery of the bonds will occur at 11:00 A.M. Thursday at the Chase National Bank.

Friday, October 27th: The bankers on Thursday in New York supplied the magic key of money to unlock a great new all-Florida gateway at Jacksonville. "This is a grand day for Florida," exclaimed Governor Warren as he exchanged bonds of the Jacksonville expressway for a small slip of pink paper bearing the figures of $27,496,960.28.

Friday, December 1st: Road officials pleased with bids on span.

Bethlehem Steel Company bid low on the steel superstructure at $7,376,712.

Merritt Chapman and Scott Corportion of New York submitted the apparent low offer of $3,588,959 to build the substructure of the bridge—the pier foundations and piers.

Thursday, December 28th: The contract between the State Road Department and Merritt-Chapman Scott Corporation in the amount of $3,588,959 for construction of the Arlington Bridge substructure was executed in Tallahassee yesterday, setting the last week of May 1952 as deadline for completion of the work.

Friday, December 29th: The contract for the construction of the superstructure for the Arlington span in the amount of $7,376,712 was executed yesterday in Tallahassee by the State Road Department and Bethlehem Steel Company and established a completion date of December 29, 1952.

The Expressway System as contemplated under the 1950 Bond Issue

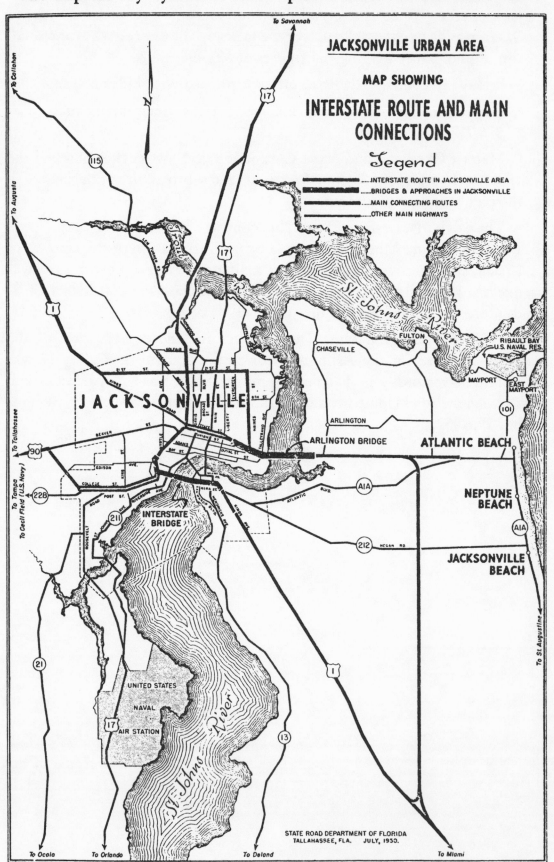

CHAPTER XIII

1950 Bonds — From Official Statement

Excerpt from Official Statement Florida State Improvement Commission of the State of Florida relating to the public offering of $28,000,000 Florida State Improvement Commission, Jacksonville expressway revenue bonds dated October 1, 1950 to be sold Monday, September 25, 1950 at the Caldwell Building, Tallahassee, Florida for delivery October 26, 1950.

Article I
Florida State Improvement Resolution

(E) That tolls, fares or other charges are to be fixed, established and collected for the use of the Arlington and interstate bridges; that no tolls, fares or other charges are to be fixed, established or collected for the use of the remaining parts of the system.

(F) That the State Road Department of Florida has agreed to contribute to the cost of construction of said system, the estimated aggregate amount of said contribution being the sum of $13,818,000.

(L) "Duval County gasoline tax funds" shall mean all the 80 percent surplus gasoline tax funds accruing in each year to the State Road Department of Florida for the use in Duval County under the provisions of Section 16 of Article IX of the Constitution of Florida, after deduction only of the first $40,000 of such gasoline tax funds, or such part thereof as shall be necessary to comply with the prior pledge of such gasoline tax funds in each year, to the payment of the principal of and interest on $4,600,000 toll road revenue bonds heretofore issued by Fernandina Port Authority under date of November 1, 1948.

Agreement by and Between the Board of County Commissioners of Duval County, Florida and the State Road Department of Florida.

Article V
Covenants of the Department

5.02. COMPLETION OF ARLINGTON AND INTERSTATE BRIDGES. The department irrevocably convenants with the commission and the holders of said bonds to be issued by the commission that if for any reason the moneys deposited in the "Bridge Construction Trust Fund" shall be insufficient to complete and place in operation said Arlington and interstate bridges, and the approaches thereto, the department will, from sources other than tolls derived from the operation of said bridges, and said Duval County gasoline tax funds, complete the construction of both said bridges and approaches thereto, so that both bridges will be completed and placed in operation at the earliest possible date.

5.03. COMPLETION OF SYSTEM. That in addition the department further covenants and agrees to complete the construction of the entire system within a reasonable time and as early as practicable after the issuance of said bonds by the commission (Florida State Improvement Commission).

THE YEARS 1951-1952

The Florida Times-Union carried the following news items during the calendar years of 1951 and 1952.

Thursday, January 25, 1951: One of the last major obstacles facing Duval County's $50,000,000 expressway was dissolved yesterday in Tallahassee as the State Road Board agreed to pay $125,000 for a strip of land 180 feet wide to be used for the southern approach of the Gilmore Street Bridge. Alfred A. McKethan, chairman of the Road Board, announced that negotiations between the State Road Department and the Baptist Hospital in Jacksonville had been successful.

Chairman McKethan has pointed out that the original cost of the expressway has risen from $41,818,000 to $50,000,000 due to rising costs.

Thursday, March 22, 1951: The State Road Department received an apparent low bid from Industrial Contracting Company of Minneapolis yesterday to build the Gilmore Street Bridge for $5,469,176.59. The bid exceeded the Road Department's estimate by approximately $867,000.

Saturday, March 24, 1951: Bids received for the construction of the Gilmore Street Bridge were rejected by the State Road Department yesterday because the apparent low bid of $5,469,176 was 1/9 per cent higher than the engineer's estimated cost.

Saturday, March 31, 1951: The State Road Board will open new bids on the Gilmore Street Bridge in Jacksonville, April 12, in the hope of getting an overall price near the $4,602,000 which engineers feel the structure should cost.

Saturday, April 21, 1951: The State Road Department yesterday in Tallahassee tossed out for the second time a combined bid for building a substructure and superstructure of the Gilmore Street Bridge but cleared the way for a start on the project by awarding a contract covering the substructure alone.

Contract for building the substructure went to Diamond Construction Company in Washington, D.C. on a low bid of $1,179,668 which was $181,000 below the estimates of State Road Department engineers.

Saturday, April 28, 1951: Alfred A. McKethan, chairman of the State Road Board, Friday in Tallahassee, advised by letter members of the Duval County legislative delegation and a Jacksonville civic organization, the Southside Business Men's Club, that work on the $50,000,000 Jacksonville Expressway was well within the Road Department's construction schedule, and that no one phase of the project would be favored over another in completing it.

McKethan wrote, "It is the purpose and the aim of the State Road Department to have these essential roadways leading to and from bridges and viaducts completed at about the time that bridges and viaducts are completed so that public convenience and necessity will best be served."

Friday, August 3, 1951: The contract for construction of the Gilmore Street Bridge superstructure was awarded on Thursday to Allied Structural Steel Company of Chicago and Industrial Contracting Company of Minneapolis, which submitted a joint low bid of $4,114,696 to the Road Board on July 24th.

Wednesday, August 15th: The Board of County Commissioners on Tuesday joined with the city of Jacksonville in consenting to the designation of the superhighway as a "limited access" road and authorized the State Road Department to establish the points along the roadways where access to it may be gained.

Thursday, November 1, 1951: Bids for constructing the final link of superhighway between Mathews Bridge and Greenland on Phillips Highway (U.S. 1) will be received by the State Road Department in Tampa, November 15, it was announced yesterday by State Road Department Chairman, Alfred A. McKethan.

Wednesday, November 29, 1951: J. Glover Taylor, local member of the State Road Board, said yesterday there will be adequate financing for the Jacksonville superhighway project during 1952.

He gave his assurance after a study of questions raised at a conference he held with members of the Chamber of Commerce Highway Committee earlier this month when the financial status of the multi-million dollar project was debated.

The chamber group asked when state and federal moneys will be put into the projects, now financed entirely by the $28 million bond issue.

Although the new state road budget will not be adopted until February, Taylor said he is certain funds will become available as needed. He asked local groups to cooperate in appearing before the board to request moneys in the 1952 budget.

It also has been established, Taylor said, that "we can buy right of way out of state funds" in case the bond issue money runs out before all necessary right of way sections are purchased.

Friday, December 1, 1951: Bethlehem Steel Company erection crews yesterday began the job of putting together the thousands of pieces of steel which will make up the superstructure of the John E. Mathews Bridge.

The first steel beam was swung into place at the cast abutment in Arlington about 10:30 A.M.

Tuesday, January 8, 1952: Merritt-Chapman and Scott Corporation yesterday started pouring a block of concrete containing almost 4500 cubic yards as part of the Mathews Bridge Pier 1-E.

Saturday, February 23, 1952: With the deadline almost at hand for completion of the State Road Department's new budget, State Road Department Chairman Alfred A. McKethan yesterday was noncommittal as to whether funds will be included to continue work on the Jacksonville expressway system.

During a meeting with local officials in Tallahassee last week, McKethan warned that if the city did not provide approximately a million dollars this year to move utilities crossing the superhighway right of way, several million dollars earmarked for expressway use in 1952 might be channeled into State Road Department projects in other areas when the budget was fixed.

Tuesday, February 26, 1952: The State Road Board yesterday in Tallahassee refused to release state and federal funds for the Jacksonville expressway in 1952 unless the city of Jacksonville moves its utilities on expressway routes.

The board left in its budget the six million dollars of federal and state funds it had budgeted for construction of the expressway in 1952.

Chairman McKethan said he felt that the city of Jacksonville had adequate notice about moving the utilities. He said the Road Department had files of former Senator John E. Mathews, Sr., now a member of the Supreme Court of Florida and these files "show that the city attorney was fully notified about moving the utilities."

Wednesday, February 27, 1952: The City Council last night adopted a resolution declaring its refusal "to entertain tax notions" proposed by Governor Fuller Warren and State Road Department Chairman, Alfred A. McKethan for raising funds to pay the expense of moving public utilities intersecting the Jacksonville expressway system.

Friday, February 29, 1952: Chairman Alfred A. McKethan of the State Road Department on Thursday called on the Jacksonville Chamber of Commerce to help solve the controversy around the relocation of utilities on the route of the Jacksonville expressway.

McKethan showed no inclination to modify the Road Board's stand. It has said the city of Jacksonville must move the utilities or state road funds will be withheld.

The Road Board chairman termed as a camouflage and smoke screen the contention of some Jacksonville officials that the city is not responsible for relocation of utilities because it was not adequately notified.

And, McKethan said the Road Department could complete approaches to the two major bridges across the St. Johns River, make the spans available for the collection of tolls and "keep full faith with the bond holders."

"The balance of the system, if not completed," said McKethan, "would be a loss to Jacksonville certainly, but would not affect the paying of the bonds to any appreciable degree."

These views were set forth today by McKethan in a letter to Brown L. Whatley, chairman of the Highway Committee of the Jacksonville Chamber of Commerce.

Wednesday, March 12, 1952: The City Council promised last night to give "prompt and earnest consideration to such budgetary transfer of funds as may be recommended to it by the City Commission" for the purpose of paying the cost of relocating utilities which interfere with expressway construction this year.

The action followed by one night a declaration by Commissioner J. Dillon Kennedy that he believes $304,000 could be provided for moving electric and water utilities in 1952 by transferring money from budgetary accounts in the Utilities Department.

Commissioner Ernest Haselden, however, said no budgetary funds were available for moving $40,000 worth of sewers and Mayor-Commissioner Haydon Burns made the same statement in regard to $100,000 needed to move Signal Bureau facilities.

The commissioners spoke at a joint meeting of City, County, State Road Board and Chamber of Commerce officials who met Monday night to discuss Jacksonville's policy in the expressway crisis.

Friday, August 1, 1952: The Jacksonville Chamber of Commerce's Highway Committee yesterday took action to speed up local highway projects, endorsed the proposed Jacksonville-to-Miami toll turnpike and called for a reorganization of the State Road Board.

Resolutions were adopted urging the state to put construction of the Trout River Bridge, and expressway link, and the improvement of Hendricks Avenue and San Jose Boulevard under contract this year.

The actions were taken after Brown L. Whatley, Committee Chairman, reported that he had received information that the state may table these projects this year. If that happens, he said, there may be no funds for them next year, when a new state administration takes office.

Whatley said he had been told that plans for the Trout River Bridge, a connection in the expressway route from the Gilmore Street Bridge to U.S. Highway 17 north of the city, have been completed but that the Road Department has given no indication it will let a contract for the project this year.

Tuesday, August 19, 1952: State Road Chairman Alfred A. McKethan disclosed here yesterday that various proposed state road projects in Jacksonville and Duval County had been delayed because of lack of funds.

He told a conference of local government and civic officials in City Hall that fiscal commitments on the Jacksonville expressway are of "such magnitude" that the state probably will be unable to put the other projects under contract this year.

These include widening of Hendricks Avenue and Lem Turner Road and the resurfacing of Atlantic Boulevard.

Friday, November 21, 1952: Skyrocketing cost will prevent completion of several vital lengths in the Jacksonville expressway unless about $39 million in additional funds can be obtained from some source, State Road Board Chairman, Alfred A. McKethan revealed yesterday in Tallahassee.

The stunning news that the big project cannot be finished with funds now in sight was disclosed in a prepared statement from McKethan to his fellow members of the Road Board.

In effect, McKethan explained, the project's cost has zoomed from a much lower original estimate to about $69 million under present circumstances. Of the big increase, almost $10 million results from boosts in right of way costs as compared to original estimates.

So far, some $30,000,000 has been spent on the program.

McKethan said, however, that it was never contemplated on finishing the expressway in less than seven or eight years.

"The orderly construction of the expressway system can be continued from year to year as regular road funds are allocated to the project, matched with federal urban funds, but construction cannot begin until the right of way is acquired," he asserted.

Money is available to complete the John E. Mathews Bridge, the Gilmore Street Bridge and approaches from Park Street on the west, to San Marco Boulevard on the east, the expressway from the east end of the John E. Mathews Bridge to U.S. Highway 1, and from the west end of the John E. Mathews Bridge to the north and south route via Main Street.

However, here are some phases of the plan which McKethan said cannot be carried out with funds now available or in sight:

1. The Myrtle Avenue Viaduct.

2. The South Jacksonville Expressway from the east end of San Marco to U.S. 1.

3. The expressway from the west end of the Gilmore Street Bridge to the Myrtle Avenue Viaduct, with connections to U.S. Highway 17 and U.S. Highway 90.

4. The South Expressway from the Myrtle Avenue Viaduct to U.S. 17 in the vicinity of the Thomas C. Imeson Airport, with new bridge over Trout River.

Friday, November 21, 1952: County Commissioner Bob Gordon, who was one of the leading figures in negotiations on the expressway project, last night expressed surprise at State Road Board Chairman Alfred A. McKethan's statement that an additional $39,000,000 would be needed from some source in order to complete the program.

"So far as I can see, the taxpayers of Duval County are not involved in any deficit that may exist in the expressway building fund," Gordon declared.

"We made a bargain with the State Road Department," Gordon explained. "It was agreed that if Duval County would pledge $28,000,000 of its surplus gas tax funds, the State Road Department would complete the entire project. There was no contingent clause which said Duval County might be called upon for additional contributions—it was understood throughout the negotiations that the $28,000,000 bond issue would be this county's sole contribution."

Gordon went on to say that Duval County had kept its part of the bargain and that the $28,000,000 bond issue had been validated both by the Duval County Circuit Courts and the State Supreme Court.

"The resolutions and agreements which plainly show that Duval County's financial responsibility ended with the $28,000,000 bond issue, and which specifically obligate the Road Department to provide whatever remaining funds are necessary to complete the project, were made a part of court records during the validation proceedings," he commented.

Gordon also pointed out that where Duval County's contribution amounts to $28,000,000, only about $30,000,000 has been spent on the expressway up to now.

Wednesday, November 26, 1952: The Florida Road Department on Tuesday awarded a $339,168 contract for construction of the east and west approaches to the Gilmore Street Bridge.

Wednesday, November 26, 1952: Chairman Alfred A. McKethan of the Florida Road Board yesterday in Tallahassee assured the people of Jacksonville that bond revenue projects of the Jacksonville expressway project would be completed in full.

McKethan said there had been some misunderstanding about the revenue bond portion of the expressway, and he desired to make plain the fact that bond-financed portions are under contract and will be completed as planned.

He also said that most of the bond financed projects will be completed ahead of schedule. He cited the John E. Mathews Bridge, which is being finished a year ahead of schedule.

Saturday, December 20, 1952: The mounting cost of rights of way is the "one definite alarming factor" in construction of the Jacksonville expressway, Chairman Alfred A. McKethan of the Florida Road Board said yesterday in Tallahassee.

Otherwise, said McKethan, the remainder of the 42-mile roadway and bridge system is progressing normally—with completion to be expected in seven to ten years.

These views were expressed today by McKethan as he presented a report to the new Florida Road Board appointed by Governor-elect Dan T. McCarty. The new board, headed by Richard H. Simpson of Monticello, will replace the Warren-appointed board January 6th.

The two boards—one outgoing and one incoming—met today jointly in Tallahassee.

Tuesday, December 30, 1952: The Jacksonville expressway's largest single structure, the $11,000,000 John E. Mathews Bridge across the St. Johns River will be dedicated New Year's Day.

County Road and Bridge Projects – 1930's

McGirts Cr. Bridge - Jax Heights Rd. Looking West. November 10, 1936

Just completed hand excavated ditch in the north branch of Little 6 Mile Creek - looking south from Mays Road on January 23, 1934

McGirts Cr. Bridge on Jax Heights Rd. Looking East. November 27, 1936

CHAPTER XV

THE YEAR 1953 — THE McCARTY TERM

The roller coaster news concerning the Jacksonville expressway from 1947 through 1952 gave the people of Duval County alternating feelings of despair and joy.

When all appeared to be going along smoothly, there would be a pessimistic and critical announcement emanating from the State Road Board in Tallahassee, for former optimistic utterances of officialdom would be replaced with resounding reneging statements.

What started out in Tallahassee in 1949 as a very favorable and beautiful relationship ended rather abruptly at the beginning of 1953 with the incoming Governor McCarty regime, for the promises received by the local citizens from the Warren administration were quickly shattered. The question in the minds of the citizens of Jacksonville was: Would the expressway project be revived and when would it be completed?

Such troubled thoughts were temporarily put aside for, on Thursday, January 1, 1953, the people of Duval County participated in the dedication of the long sought-for bridge spanning the St. Johns River from Jacksonville to the Arlington area.

Climax of the ceremony came when Mrs. John E. Mathews unveiled a plaque naming the bridge in her husband's honor.

Shortly thereafter, with a snip of a pair of gold plated scissors, Mrs. Mathews cut the ribbon barrier to the bridge named for her distinguished husband, Supreme Court Justice John E. Mathews.

In his address Justice Mathews made this significant statement:

"Should the men and women of the present generation begin today with the thought and idea that another bridge, or bridges, will be necessary in the not too distant future, it would require many years to convince the people of this necessity, to agree upon sites and whether bridges or tunnels would best serve the purpose. After sufficient unity had been achieved and a majority of the people have agreed upon a plan, it will then take many more years to develop the details and to finance such a plan and for engineers to prepare plans and specifications which would be agreed upon by responsible authorities."

In addition to Brown Whatley, who presided at the ceremony, were Governor Fuller Warren, Chairman Alfred McKethan of the State Road Board and J. Glover Taylor of Jacksonville, a member of the State Road Board. The State Improvement Commission was represented by Charles W. Blum of Jacksonville, a member and J. Turner Butler, the commission's attorney.

Three members of the County Commission—Chairman Joe F. Hammond, C. Ray Greene and Edward I. Acosta together with the board's attorney, J. Henry Blount and County Engineer Arthur N. Sollee, looked on with pride.

Mayor Haydon Burns headed the city officials at the ceremony. That group included Commissioners Ernest S. Haselden and J. Dillon Kennedy, President James M. Peeler of the City Council, Captain William E. Sheddan, city engineer consultant, and City Engineer Walter F. Daniel.

The Mathews Bridge was designed by Reynolds, Smith and Hills of Jacksonville and Parsons, Brinckerhoff, Hall and Macdonald of New York City, jointly serving as associates, architects and engineers. Members of those firms present included John F. Reynolds, George B. Hills and P.M. Huddleston of the Jacksonville firm and Eugene L. Macdonald of the New York group.

The George D. Auchter Company of Jacksonville, which built eight piers under the west approach structure, was represented by James T. Monahan, executive vice president.

R.I. Senn represented Merritt, Chapman and Scott of New York City, principal contractors for the rest of the substructure.

D.S. Blankenship represented the Bethlehem Steel Co., contractor for the final phase of the bridge—the superstructure.

Others present included Richey Green, project engineer for the State Road Department, and W.E. Dean, engineer of bridges.

The new State Road Board appointed by Governor Dan McCarty, at their first meeting on Tuesday, January 7, 1953 indicated it did not intend to build the Myrtle Avenue overpass in Jacksonville soon.

The S.R.D. told Jacksonville Highway Commissioner Ernest Haselden it favored the Gilmore Street Bridge to U.S. Highway 1 rather than to construct the $2,500,000 overpass.

S.R.D. Chairman Simpson, commenting on the commitment by the Warren administration of all of the $28,000,000 expressway bond issue, said:

"You have got the east part built. The bond money is spent. The rest of it has to come the hard way." S.R.D. member J. Saxton Lloyd said: "The last Road Board started the San Marco overpass with the idea of forcing this board to finish it. That is why I am not inclined to continue on with it and have it hanging in mid-air."

Simpson suggested a 30-day waiting period in order to give Haselden a chance to talk about it with Jacksonville officials.

Questioned by Haselden, Simpson stated the Road Department could connect the Gilmore Street Bridge to U.S. Highway 1 (Philips Highway) as the department's thinking was to the south rather than going on to the north.

The real shocker came at a luncheon in the Mayflower Hotel on Friday, January 23, 1953, sponsored by the Highway Committee of the Jacksonville Chamber of Commerce. Richard Simpson, chairman of the State Road Board, was the luncheon speaker. He told the gathering: "The honeymoon is over for the Jacksonville expressway." He noted the expressway had a deficit of $2.25 million which must be paid for in 1953. He explained the deficit as follows:

A total of $30.6 million had been spent or committed on expressway projects completed or under contract. Bonds sold to finance the project, plus their accrued interest, gave a credit of $28.35 million, leaving a deficit of $2.25 million. Of the $2.25 million, the amount of $1.57 million was from Road Department primary funds, the remaining $680,000 from federal funds.

Simpson said 1954 may offer a "brighter picture" in Road Department finances.

As a result of Simpson's remarks the Chamber's Highway Committee adopted a proposed priority of construction schedule.

This schedule was adopted by a special committee of local government and business leaders over objections of the county commissioners.

On January 30, in Tallahassee, the S.R.D. awarded a contract for the construction of the substructure of the Myrtle Avenue overpass and at the same time rejected a bid for the superstructure.

Appearing at this meeting was Fred Kent, vice chairman of the Jacksonville Chamber of Commerce Committee on Roads, who termed the Myrtle Avenue overpass "the nerve center of the expressway and added it would relieve 'intolerable' traffic conditions."

Simpson said, "I would like to complete the entire expressway next year and get it out of the way. If the money becomes available we may be able to finish the project in eight, six or even five years."

The *Jacksonville Journal* in an editorial in the Wednesday April 1, 1953 issue summed up the feelings of the community as follows:

The bad news coming out of Jacksonville's superhighway—or by now, it should be labelled duperhighway—seems to go on and on.

Confirmation has now come that the east end of the Gilmore Street Bridge will meet San Marco Boulevard at a level intersection, dumping more traffic into the already jammed traffic artery. Gone is the pretty dream of the bridge traffic soaring over San Marco on an overpass, a thrilling picture contained in the original plans when the citizens of Duval County were duped by the old State Road Board. What's more, the east end of the bridge comes to an abrupt dead end against San Marco, meaning that traffic crossing the bridge will have to turn right or left into the San Marco traffic from two other bridges. Under the present set-up, all three of the city's downtown bridges will empty on the Southside in an area barely three blocks long.

Actually, the fact that the new bridge will dead end on San Marco should come as no surprise to Jaxons. We have been building dead end bridges for the past 35 years and now boast the distinction, probably unique in the whole world, of having three downtown bridges, all of them running into a dead end. The Acosta Bridge hits a dead end atop the Riverside Viaduct; the Main Street Bridge runs into a dead end at Miami Road; now the Gilmore Street Bridge will dead end at San Marco. Millions of dollars worth of bridges with no place to go.

The present Road Board refuses to use a "crystal ball" in trying to determine when money will be available for the San Marco overpass and some $40,000,000 construction necessary to complete the superhighway system as originally planned. Which is probably just as well. The old Road Board's crystal ball was more than somewhat clouded when it was used to conjure up a picture of a great bridge and highway system intended to relieve the traffic pressure on Jacksonville. So far, Jacksonville has gotten a couple of bridges with doubtful approaches out of the deal.

Instead of helping traffic, they seem more likely to complicate it further. No more crystal balls please.

With little fanfare the John E. Mathews bridge was opened to traffic at 10:00 A.M. Wednesday, April 15, 1953. In the initial 15 minutes of operation, 586 vehicles crossed the mile-and-half long bridge.

Under a Tallahassee Monday July 27, 1953 date line, S.R.D. Chairman Simpson was quoted as stating "local help can expedite expressway." Simpson disputed a statement by Brown L. Whatley, chairman of the Chamber of Commerce Highway Committee, that local governmental and other groups were in harmony on the expressway.

The fact that Whatley himself recently publicly protested the Road Board's philosophy "is proof in itself of my contention that a serious conference is needed between a committee of responsible Jacksonville citizens and the State Road Department," Simpson said.

A Jacksonville delegation again met with top State Road Department officials in Tallahassee on Tuesday, August 4, 1953 and presented their views. But Simpson termed the delegation's demands "next to impossible" because of the lack of road funds. He suggested creation of a five-member Jacksonville citizen's committee to work closely with the S.R.D. to help work out "acceptable solutions" to diverse views.

Whatley, speaking for the Jacksonville Chamber of Commerce Highway

Committee, said the committee would be likely to heed the proposal.

This committee was announced by Whatley on Wednesday, August 12 as being composed of Whatley himself; Fred Kent, vice chairman of the chamber highway group; State Representative Fletcher Morgan; J.K. Atwood, president of the Five Points Business Association; and Carl Taylor, chairman of the Southside Business Men's Club Highway Committee.

Speaking before the Southside Business Men's Club on Wednesday September 2, 1953, Simpson said the next expressway project should be the construction of links between the Gilmore Street bridge and Philips Highway and the Myrtle Avenue overpass to the north. He told the club that present and completed expressway projects were not eligible for federal support but would seek it. He reported that "from the start of construction through July 31 of 1953, $30,410,832 was spent on the expressway."

Simpson said Governor McCarty and the Road Board were aware of their moral commitments to build as much of the expressway as possible with funds available during their administration.

The muddled affairs of the expressway were again compounded, for Governor McCarty died within a few months and with his demise the McCarty Road Board was left in a floundering position with still countless unanswered and unsolved problems of the Jacksonville expressway.

County Road and Bridge Projects - 1930's

Looking South at McGirts Cr.
Bridge on Chaffee Road
November 7, 1936

McGirts Creek Bridge on Chaffee
Road looking South November 7,
1936

Moncrief-Dinsmore Road April 1,
1937

CHAPTER XVI
The Johns Administration

"The State Road Department is in better financial condition now and I do not foresee any serious hindrance in the expressway work," said Chairman Simpson visiting Jacksonville on November 3, 1953. He said the state would receive bids on the Myrtle Avenue overpass in December. He also told the Chamber of Commerce committee the Road Board would meet with Governor Charles E. Johns on November 18 at Tallahassee to submit a proposal for expressway expenditures in 1954. He added that at the end of the current year $7 million will have been spent on expressway contracts.

On December 5, 1953 Johns proposed an emergency shifting maneuver which would make $1.5 million more available for the Jacksonville expressway during 1954. This amount would supplement $3 million already committed, giving a total of $4.5 million expected to be spent on expressway work during the year.

Speaking in Tallahassee on December 16, Florida's new State Road Chairman, Cecil Webb, said that he considers the state "has an obligation to complete the Jacksonville expressway as quickly as possible."

The S.R.D. meeting in Tallahassee on January 29, 1954 hiked its 1954 appropriation for the Jacksonville expressway to $6,322,167 allotting $2,122,167 more than had been originally promised.

Governor Johns on April 7th ordered the Road Department to call for bids for this month on construction of the overpass spanning San Marco Boulevard and other Southside connecting links to the Gilmore Street Bridge. He also ordered a review of the Jacksonville expressway's Southside and Riverside plans to help iron out problems caused by the dead ending of streets. The expressway has stagnated long enough, he said. "We are going to make some progress."

The Gilmore Street Bridge was dedicated and opened to traffic on June 7th. In his dedication address Supreme Court Justice John E. Mathews declared it would be only a question of time before another bridge between the spot where all were standing and Green Cove Springs would be an absolute necessity.

The *Jacksonville Journal* on June 8th carried the following editorial:

Precisely how far Jacksonville has come from a one-horse town can be measured by the fact that we are now a four-bridge city.

The fact that the approaches to the Gilmore Street Bridge are far from satisfactory detracts only a little from the advantages of having a fourth bridge open across the St. Johns. The bridge connects two heavily populated areas, Riverside and Southside, and takes the load off the totally inadequate Acosta Bridge. For 15 cents, those driving from one section to the other can avoid the long delay at the Acosta-viaduct bottleneck of the "old bridge." There are doubters but our guess is that it will be worth 15 cents to many a motorist to duck that bottleneck.

Unfortunately, the bridge is unhandy for the very traffic for which it was designed, visitors seeking a quick and easy way through the city. Lack of access on the Riverside end, due to delays in construction of the Myrtle Avenue overpass and the expressway links on the north end, will cut down effectiveness of the new map as a throughway. So will the present dead ending of the bridge at San Marco, rather than overpasses and sweeping roadways connecting the south approaches into U.S. 1 South.

These approaches, and the eventual use of the bridge by interstate traffic, are well in the future. All will depend on the attitude toward the expressway by the future administration in Tallahassee.

So Jacksonville's newest bridge is born in troublesome times. But it is a most welcome addition nevertheless.

On June 15th Governor Johns agreed to a Jacksonville delegation's proposal to appoint Carl M. Taylor, Jacksonville real estate man, as a "director of the expressway" to expedite progress on the multi-million dollar project.

Urging the appointment was a four-member Jacksonville delegation, Road Board member Johnny Walker of Gainesville, State Representative Fletcher Morgan, Duval County nominee for the Senate; Representatives W. Lacy Mahon, Jr., and Harry Westberry; and Brown L. Whaley, chairman of the Chamber of Commerce Highway Committee.

Morgan said the expressway was bogged down completely and not a wheel was turning.

Whatley said the expressway seemed to lack coordination.

Johns also approved the delegation's plan to establish an expressway planning division in Jacksonville so engineers could iron out local problems on the ground.

On Wednesday, June 18th Jacksonville's five-man Expressway Citizens Committee, Brown L. Whatley, Fred Kent, J.K. Attwood, Carl Taylor and Fletcher Morgan, placed local responsibility for expressway planning in the hands of city and county engineers and agreed to abide by the engineer's decisions. They requested the city and county to permit City Consulting Engineer William E. Sheddan, City Engineer Walter J. Daniel and County Engineer Arthur N. Sollee to work with the Expressway Engineer Wesley A. Sweat and Expressway Director Carl M. Taylor in an effort to speed up the planning of the expressway.

Comments by the Duval County Engineer were publicized in *The Florida Times-Union* on July 8, 1954 in the following manner.

Creation of a state planning commission with authority to select routes for roads and schedule their orderly construction was urged yesterday by Duval County Engineer Arthur N. Sollee.

Sollee also sees the need for establishment of a planning board along similar lines for Duval County.

The need for a state planning commission, Sollee said in a talk to the Meninak Club, has been emphasized by lack of proper planning in construction of the Jacksonville expressway.

"There is no one who can say with authority where the next project of the expressway will be built," the engineer declared.

A planning commission, he pointed out, could set up orderly construction for the expressway that would be carried out without interruption by changes in a state administration.

Proper planning, Sollee argued, would greatly reduce the cost of right of way for the expressway and any other road that may be built. As an example, he pointed out that the present westerly route of the expressway calls for it to go through the new million dollar Winn-Lovett warehouse. This, he said, would be inconceivable but was a good route when plans were prepared several years ago.

Sollee also made references to planning for the two bridges—the Mathews Bridge and Gilmore Street Bridge. Out-of-state engineering firms, he said, forecast that the Gilmore Bridge would carry 1.7 times the traffic of the Arlington span. Latest figures, he stated, show the Mathews Bridge averages 10,000 vehicles daily and the Gilmore Street Bridge 8,000. (Much greater traffic is expected over the Gilmore Bridge when the expressway is completed).

Sollee said, too, that the out-of-state engineering firm failed to consider the growth of the Arlington area and set as 1982 the date when traffic over the Mathews Bridge would reach the amount crossing it today.

Duval County officials, Sollee said, long ago recognized the need for planning roads for the future, much of which was done while Earl Luce was county engineer more than 20 years ago. Sollee said this foresightedness saved taxpayers many hundreds of thousands of dollars for right of way.

He mentioned that Normandy Boulevard had been conceived as early as 1918 and established as the Gainesville short cut. This also was true of Blanding Boulevard, acquired years ago as the Old Orange Park Road. Still another example, he said, is Beach Boulevard, the right of way—

formerly the Florida East Coast Railway to the beach—having been acquired in 1937 for $8,500.

Looking ahead today, Sollee said the Board of County Commissioners recently completed acquisition of a right of way that will permit construction of a road along the river from Ft. Caroline to Mayport, opening new territory in the county. A route also has been established for a short route to the beach through the Southside at Spring Park Road, he stated.

Sollee also told of county planning in relation to zoning laws and restrictions on development of new suburbs. He emphasized that more planning in the outlying areas is needed in view of the fast growth of Duval County. Today, he said 350 or more houses are being built monthly in Duval County outside the Jacksonville city limits.

Sollee, a member of the Club, was introduced by W. Gregory Smith.

President Ira M. Koger presided at the luncheon, held in the Mayflower Hotel.

On August 16, the Florida Road Department engineers gave final approval to the rerouting of the Southside expressway calling for the overcrossing of San Marco Boulevard, Florida East Coast Railroad, Hendricks Avenue, Old Kings Road, Atlantic Boulevard at Times Square with connections to Philips Highway and Atlantic Boulevard. It was also announced that Reynolds, Smith and Hills, engineers from Jacksonville, had completed plans for the intricate expressway system in the Riverside area connecting the Gilmore Street Bridge to Osceola Street and the Myrtle Avenue overpass.

The Florida Times-Union edition of August 28, 1954 carried a story, parts of which are quoted below.

A two-year tide of opposition to expressway plans for Riverside started to turn the other way yesterday when Expressway Engineer, Wesley A. Sweat, explained newly developed plans to Riverside business and civic leaders at a meeting at Five Points.

The point on which the turnabout came was the fact that no streets would be dead ended as called for in previous plans. Instead of being closed, streets would be connected to the expressway or four major local thoroughfares—Riverside, Park, College and Forest—directly or by new service roads.

At the same time, Sweat pointed out, the expressway itself would provide a new, rapid route in all directions to and from Riverside.

When Sweat concluded his explanation, Mrs. L.M. Simpson, a housewife, jumped to her feet and exclaimed: "That's the best thing that could happen to Riverside."

Ben J. Philips, chairman of the Expressway Committee of the Greater Riverside Business Association, told a newspaper reporter that the committee thought the plans were "good."

Fletcher Morgan then took up the defense. He pointed out that the Riverside section was only a segment of the overall system and declared that "there's not a city in the South that doesn't envy Jacksonville for its expressway."

"If the Riverside project isn't started this year, you'll be throwing away two million dollars," he said, "and the job may be delayed another two years. Instead of bottling you up, it's going to give you another artery to downtown."

Morgan called attention to the fact that there apparently are no plans by the city government to ease Jacksonville's traffic problems. He therefore held out the expressway as the only known solution to those problems.

"The Road Department cooperated with you and has changed the plans so there are no dead ends or closings," he said. "Now it's up to you to decide whether you want the money spent here or give it to South Florida."

By a vote of three to two the City Commission at their meeting held on September 9, 1954 approved a limited access plan for the Riverside interchange of the Jacksonville expressway. Those voting against the measure were Mayor-Commissioner Haydon Burns and Commissioner J. Dillon Kennedy; those voting for it were Commissioners Claude Smith, Jr., Guy L. Simmons and Ernest S. Haselden.

Bids for the construction of Haines Street from Mathews Bridge interchange to Eighth Street were opened on December 7, 1954 by the State Road Department and the following day they called for bids to be opened on January 3, 1955 on the Riverside interchange sections of the expressway.

The January 3rd bid opening was to be the Johns Road Board's final meeting. The new administration of Governor LeRoy Collins would take office the next day.

With the departure of the Johns followers the hopes of all Duval County turned to the new administration of Governor LeRoy Collins.

County Road and Bridge Projects - 1930's

Looking South on Seminole Beach Road from Steel Avenue, December 3, 1935

Seminole Beach Road looking South from Old J.P. & M. RR, June 8, 1936

Seminole Beach Road looking North from Sta. 9 too, March 13, 1936

CHAPTER XVII

THE COLLINS ADMINISTRATION BEGINS

The first message of Governor LeRoy Collins concerning the Jacksonville expressway as carried in *The Florida Times-Union* on January 18, 1955, is as follows:

A message from Governor LeRoy Collins gave reassurances yesterday that he plans to fulfill a campaign promise to complete "at least the essential parts" of the Jacksonville expressway during the two-year term for which he was elected.

This statement was made in a letter read at the Duval Board of County Commissioners' meeting yesterday. It was addressed to County Engineer, Arthur N. Sollee, who had written to the governor at the time he forwarded Duval County's 1955 road building program to Collins and State Road Board members two weeks ago.

After discussing his road building program generally, Governor Collins wrote:

"I also assume I need not assure you of my determination to see that everything possible is done to complete at least the essential parts of the Jacksonville expressway within the next two years. This is the statement I made repeatedly in the campaign and I do not intend to forget it. This statement, of course, is based on the obvious place the expressway would occupy in a program giving consideration to need.

"It is not my intention, however, to attempt to dictate to our new Road Board and I am pleased to note that copies of your board's resolutions also have gone to Mr. Wilbur E. Jones and Mr. Earl Powers (Road Board Chairman and member from this district, respectively)."

On January 18, 1955, Duval County's road building program was formally submitted to the State Road Department in Lake City and while it met with favor, Earl P. Powers of Gainesville, member from this district, said the amount of money available will determine how much of it can be accomplished.

Connecting links of the Jacksonville expressway headed the list of proposed projects. Powers assured the delegation, which included members of the Board of County Commissioners, city officials and Chamber of Commerce representatives, that the project also was foremost in the minds of State Road Department officials.

Powers said the Road Board's position on the expressway was expressed by Collins in a letter to County Engineer Arthur N. Sollee, which assured "at least the essential parts" of the expressway would be completed within the next two years.

Bids had already been received for the Haines Street and Riverside links. The delegation urged the contracts be awarded, the San Marco overpass be extended across the Florida East Coast Railway right of way and the balance of the right of way be acquired for the Southside section.

On March 11, 1955 the State Road Department announced it planned to award the contract for the Riverside interchange section of the Jacksonville expressway to Duval Engineering and Contracting Company which submitted a low bid of $1,643,665 for the job. The Road Department also stated it had executed a contract for the Haines Street section of the expressway.

THE FORMATIVE PERIOD OF THE JACKSONVILLE EXPRESSWAY AUTHORITY

There was a great awakening in the early months of 1955 by the civic leaders of Jacksonville who had been closely connected with the expressway since its inception in 1946. It dawned upon them like a crash of thunder that for eight long years the promises and pledges of the policy makers and administrative heads of the Florida State Road Department had been misleading, unreliable, and easily broken.

After weeks and months of research and after many conferences it was decided that the answer was an expressway authority that would be vested with the necessary power to plan and finance its own construction programs without having to depend on the whims of the S.R.D. or the idiosyncrasies of the federal government.

Without fanfare or prior notices a legal advertisement appeared in the April 4, 1955 issue of the *Financial News and Daily Record* notifying the public that it was the intention to apply to the Legislature of the State of Florida during its 1955 session for the passage of "An Act Creating the Jacksonville Expressway Authority and Defining its Jurisdiction and Powers."

The full advertisement was signed by Morgan, senator from Duval County.

The general public had no inkling what was being contemplated until the news broke in the May 19 issue of *The Florida Times-Union*. The headlines on one page read, "Duval Board Opposes Refinance Proposal" while on another page headlines said, "Board Urged to Back Plan for Highway— Chamber Asks County to Reconsider Expressway Refinance Plan."

During the next few days the county commissioners conferred with their attorney and county engineer and then at a meeting held on May 23, agreed to support the expressway authority bill but issued a statement on its position regarding proposed legislation creating the Jacksonville Expressway Authority, a part of which is recorded as follows:

1. In the resolution of December 2, 1949 among other things, it was provided:

    "It is further understood and agreed that any surplus gasoline tax income in excess of the requirements for debt service and reserve funds shall be distributed as provided by law."

    This aforesaid provision was added upon the insistence of this board at that time and materially affected the decision of the board in finally passing the resolution wherein it requested the $28 million bond issue. However, in the subsequent proceedings had by the State

Road Department and the Florida State Improvement Commission, this vital provision, insisted upon by the county commissioners, was ignored and entirely forgotten and the result was that Duval County, under the present bond setup, is forever barred from receiving any excess surplus gasoline tax over and above annual requirement, until the full $28 million is paid.

2.   The resolution of December 2, 1949 was predicated upon positive assurances that the county commissioners had from the State Road Department that the said State Road Department would:

(a)   Make available toward the construction of the expressway the sum of $13,818,000; and,

(b)   Would complete the construction of the entire system within a reasonable time and as early as practical after issuance of the bonds by the Improvement Commission.

3.   That the county commissioners at considerable expense, furnished to the State Road Department, subsequent to the adoption of the resolution of December 2, 1949, a well-considered program and plan of construction. However, the State Road Department did not use this plan. Nevertheless, the Board of County Commissioners, prior to the adoption of the resolution of December 2, 1949, was adamant in its position that the Arlington Bridge (now Mathews Bridge) should become a component part of the system. But for the position so taken by the county commissioners, the Mathews Bridge would not be in existence today.

4.   The construction of the expressway up to this time has not been planned in an orderly manner and as a result, considerable loss has been incurred. In making this statement, reference is made to the position of the Fuller Warren Bridge, with no feeder road connections to the bridge; and the acquisition of many parcels of land for rights of way, which up to this time have not been utilized for the purposes for which they were acquired.

In view of the above, which are only a few matters which could be enumerated, the Board of County Commissioners is definitely not going to enter into any agreement or pass any resolution requesting the refinancing of the present bond issue unless and until this board has absolute proof, duly documented, that will guarantee the completion of the expressway out of the funds to be raised in the refinancing plan and from monies to be furnished by the State Road Department of Florida and federal monies available to the State Road Department. And, further, that this board be assured that it will be supplied, from time to time, with pertinent information showing in detail the development and progress of the contemplated project and the planning therefor. Also, that this board be given definite assurances that the present and future primary road system in Duval County will not be seriously penalized to the detriment of the traveling public.

Now, with the assurance that the legislative delegation has given this board, coupled with the esteem in which they are held by the county commissioners, as the duly elected representatives of the people of the county, this board, by appropriate motion to be taken today, will stipulate its approval of the proposed legislation and will, at the appropriate time, adopt the necessary resolutions which will pave the way in activating the construction and completion of the expressway.

The next day the State Road Department agreed it would contribute at least $12 million toward the completion of the Jacksonville expressway.

After having passed the Senate and House the bill creating the Jacksonville Expressway Authority was signed into law on Thursday, June 23, 1955 by Governor LeRoy Collins. As he signed the bill he was watched by the Duval County legislative delegation of Representatives William Maness, Harry W. Westberry and W. Lacy Mahon, Jr., and Senator Fletcher Morgan. Road Board Chairman Wilbur Jones also was present.

On July 23, 1955 while Governor Collins was in Jacksonville on his way to New York, he announced the names of the appointees to the newly created Jacksonville Expressway Authority. They were Lucius A. Buck, 326 Ocean Boulevard, Atlantic Beach, a member of the legal firm of Buck and Drew; Irving J. Pemberton, 4205 Ortega Boulevard, Vice President of the W.H. Clark Fruit Company and James H. O'Reilly, 4936 Apache Avenue, head of an investment firm in Jacksonville.

The governor said commissions of appointment would be issued when he returned to the state the following week.

While in New York the governor on July 25 sent a telegram to Lucius A. Buck designating him as the chairman of the new authority and told him to "proceed with organization as you feel the exigencies require."

The first meeting of the authority was held on August 12, 1955. It agreed that it must obtain a feasibility report "from engineers and fiscal experts as a means to bring about the speedy completion of the expressway."

A preliminary report toward that end was given by Earl P. Powers of Gainesville, an ex-officio member as a member of the State Road Board, who was asked to look into the matter by Chairman Lucius A. Buck.

Powers revealed that he had negotiated with the engineering firm of Coverdale and Colpitts of New York to make a survey of traffic and earnings; with Reynolds, Smith and Hills of Jacksonville to prepare a cost study in association with W.H. Lochner of Chicago; and with the investment firm of Pierce, Carrison and Wulbern, Inc., of Jacksonville to study the fiscal and bond-marketing problems in association with Smith and Barney of New York.

The authority agreed that these firms would be engaged to do the work if they could get together on the price.

Action also was deferred on the appointment of the authority's executive director, the general counsel and an assistant general counsel.

The Jacksonville Expressway Authority on September 1, 1955 approved contracts for engineering services with Reynolds, Smith and Hills, W.H. Lochner, and Coverdale and Colpitts, for traffic surveys to determine the revenue potential of the toll bridges.

Smith, Barney and Company of New York with the Jacksonville investment firm of Pierce, Carrison and Wulbern, were named bankers for the authority with priority to purchase the revenue bonds.

For the next seven months the authority routinely:

1. Authorized traffic engineers to proceed with traffic and cost studies of the expressway.

2. Requested the S.R.D. to include in its 1956 work budget an extension of the Myrtle Avenue link of the expressway from Church Street to Beaver Street.

3. Received the engineers and bankers reports which estimated the cost of completing the expressway at $49,802,290.

CHAPTER XIX

THE 1957 REVENUE BOND PROGRAM

But Chrysippus, Posidonius, Zeno, and Boethus say, that all things are produced by fate. And fate is a connected cause of existing things, or the reason according to which the world is regulated.

Diogenes Laertius

The Florida Times-Union edition of Tuesday, March 27, 1956 reporting on county courthouse events printed a news item, excerpts of which are as follows:

Arthur N. Sollee was named yesterday as executive director of the Jacksonville Expressway Authority.

His appointment came after weeks of search for a director. The announcement created some surprise when Sollee tendered his resignation as county engineer to the Board of County Commissioners yesterday afternoon.

John H. Crosby, who has been assistant county engineer since Oct. 1, 1953, was named county engineer to succeed Sollee.

"Learned of Availability"

"We have searched far and wide for a man we felt competent to fill the job of executive director," Authority Chairman Lucius A. Buck said. "It was just a few days ago that we learned that Mr. Sollee was available and we immediately entered into negotiations with him. We believe we have obtained the finest man possible for the job and feel sure his appointment will mean progress on the expressway can go ahead much faster."

Buck said it means that Wesley A. Sweat, who has had to double as chief engineer and acting director, can now give his full time to the engineering phases of the project.

Sweat was obtained from the State Road Department soon after the expressway Authority was organized last summer. Because no one else was available, Sweat agreed to assume the duties of acting director until one could be found.

"Too Much for One Man"

"We have come too far now for one man to do both jobs," Buck said. "We feel we have solved an important part of our organization."

Sollee will begin his duties with the Expressway Authority next Monday. He will officially retire from the county at the end of his vacation period on April 21.

In taking the position with the Expressway Authority, Sollee accepts a job with which he already is familiar. As county engineer he had a part in planning and development of the expressway, including the completed route through Arlington and Southside Estates.

County commissioners have recognized that Sollee, by foresight in planning, has saved taxpayers hundreds of thousands of dollars in right of way acquisition. Upon his recommendation commissioners over a period of years have acquired right of way for future road and bridge construction at a time when the price was low. Many county road and bridge projects were planned and constructed under his supervision.

I had no knowledge that the Expressway Authority was seeking a director until I was approached by County Commission Chairman C. Ray Greene who said he had recommended me for the position and if I were interested, to contact Mr. James H. O'Reilly, a member of the authority, for an interview.

The meeting with Mr. O'Reilly on Friday, March 23 was a very pleasant one and it turned out to be the beginning of a most cherished friendship with a perfect gentleman and astute financier.

On Monday, April 2, 1956, I began my duties as the executive director of the Jacksonville Expressway Authority.

By a happy circumstance Chairman Lucius A. Buck of the authority was a personal friend of Governor Collins and this relationship was a great contributing cause in the successful building of the local expressway system.

Some several weeks prior to the sale of the expressway bonds, Cheever Hardwick of Smith, Barney and Company, New York financial investment firm said the fact that Collins would be governor for another four years "will be a very important factor in the sale of the expressway bonds."

"Your governor," said Hardwick, "has been very astute in trying to bring business and industry to your state. He has made it known everywhere he has been in and out of Florida that he is running the state on a business administration. I have heard him spoken of highly by bankers and industrialists in all parts of the country and it seems quite evident that he has made a very marked impression on some of the nation's business leaders."

It was a momentous occasion on April 9, 1957 for the $70 million revenue bonds issue was sold to help finance completion of the Jacksonville expressway system. A check in the amount of $68,892,606.67 was delivered to the authority on May 1st in New York City as net payment for the multi-million dollar issue.

No recording of the history of the Jacksonville expressway would be complete without the precise and knowledgeable commentary of James C. Craig which is reproduced as it appeared in the April 14, 1957 edition of *The Florida Times-Union*.

Cut the flowers and bind them into bunches. It's bouquet throwing time on the Jacksonville expressway.

Last Tuesday the Jacksonville Expressway Authority sold $70 million worth of revenue bonds to refinance an earlier $28 million issue and to provide funds for completing the huge roadway. The interest rate which averaged 4.3 per cent wasn't as low as was wished for but was considered quite creditable in view of current market conditions.

It took two years of planning, perseverence and work to get those bonds sold and everybody who had anything at all to do with it deserves the thanks of a public that should be ever grateful.

Two years ago the expressway was sputtering out. The $28 million was gone along with what looked like the last of state and federal funds. For its money, the people had the John E. Mathews Bridge with a divided highway extending from Main Street and an alternate U.S. Highway 1 that circumvented traffic congestion of downtown Jacksonville and the Southside, rejoining Philips Highway at Greenland. There also was being completed an offshoot of that route extending along Haines Street from the bridge approach to Eighth Street.

Along the main part of the proposed expressway—the north-south route—the Fuller Warren Bridge had been built, but served no useful purpose because it connected with nothing. An overpass on Myrtle Avenue was about half finished, but there was no rush about completing it because it couldn't be used. The contract had just been let for the Riverside interchange.

That was all Jacksonville had to show for its money and the chances of getting the expressway finished looked dim, indeed. But there was one man who refused to go along with the defeatists and came up with the idea that turned a bright light on the whole expressway. Pick out the biggest bouquet in the pile and toss it to: State Sen. Fletcher Morgan.

Sen. Morgan discussed his idea of refinancing the inadequate bond issue with financial experts and bond attorneys. They then told him his plan was feasible, he went to Tallahassee and presented it to Gov. LeRoy Collins. The governor deserves a bouquet, too, because he lent the plan his immediate support and has continued to help all along the way. Another bouquet belongs to State Road Board Chairman Wilbur Jones, who also has gone along with the idea.

With the top state officials on his side, Sen. Morgan then "sold" the plan to his legislative colleagues—Reps. Lacy Mahon, Jr., Harry Westberry and William H. Maness. They put the bill through the 1955 Legislature creating the Jacksonville Expressway Authority.

The act directed that the governor appoint three members and that this district's member of the State Road Board and the chairman of the Duval

Board of County commissioners serve as ex-officio members. All serve without pay. So sort through the pile and come up with five of the finest bouquets for these men.

It would be difficult to place a value on the services that Lucius A. Buck has rendered to the expressway project. As he is chairman of the authority, the heaviest load has fallen on his shoulders. It seems certain that without his leadership, drive and determination, the date of the bond sale probably would still be months away. And he has done this at the personal sacrifice of this private law practice.

Also making a personal sacrifice and giving perhaps as much time as Chairman Buck has been James H. O'Reilly, who deals in investments. O'Reilly is the authority's secretary.

The other gubernatorial appointee, Irving J. Pemberton, has been in ill health during a good bit of his tenure on the authority. Nevertheless, when necessary, he has let his wholesale produce business take a second place to the expressway business.

Although from Gainesville, Earl P. Powers, who sits on the authority because he is the 2nd District's member of the State Road Board, could have been no more faithful to the expressway had he been a resident of Duval County. He has seen to it that the State Road Department advanced all funds necessary to the authority. He has helped work for a larger part of federal aid funds. And he has cut red tape in the way of getting right of way acquisition and construction plans through the S.R.D. channels.

There has been no attempt to list those due bouquets in order of their contributions, so just because C. Ray Greene is mentioned last doesn't mean that's where he belongs by any means. There should be one big combination bouquet for all members of the Duval Board of County Commissioners, who have cooperated to the fullest by pledging necessary gasoline tax revenue to finance bonds.

And the county commissioners also should be commended for electing Greene as permanent chairman of the board so he could continue as a member of the Expressway Authority because of his familiarity with the program. And that gesture has already paid off. Through Greene's personal efforts Duval County will start getting back some of its gas funds for needed work on primary roads much earlier than was originally proposed.

Through his efforts, too, the east-west route, which will extend from U.S. 1 to an interchange with the north-south route, following 20th and 21st streets to Haines Street, was not shunted into the back seat. It is scheduled for completion within the next three years. So see that Greene gets a special bouquet.

Bouquets also should be distributed to the attorneys, engineers and members of the administrative staff, but they have been paid for their services. Those singled out here for special commendation haven't received the first red cent for what they have done, nor will they.

So sow some more flower seeds because there probably will be others deserving of bouquets—and it is entirely likely that a second round of posies will be due those designated to get the first.

Mr. Craig's last statement could not have been more prophetic for all of the sections specified to be built under the $70 million bond program were constructed efficiently and expeditiously.

The sections were part of Interstate 10 from Interstate 95 at the Riverside interchange west to Lane Avenue; the expressway from Interstate 10 to Roosevelt Boulevard; and Interstate 95 from Dunn Avenue southerly to connections with Atlantic Boulevard and Philips Highway, including Trout River Bridge, but excluding Fuller Warren Bridge which was built under the 1950 bond program.

The authority also was in a financial position to upgrade the 20th Street section of the expressway between Interstate 95 and Haines Street, a section of the Arlington Expressway and rebuild the Gator Bowl interchange to modern standards.

Therefore, the second round of posies certainly was well earned and richly deserved by Governor Collins, Chairman Buck, Secretary O'Reilly and members Pemberton, Powers and Greene.

Chairman Buck, a tax attorney, was a stickler for accuracy and efficiency. Knowing it was difficult to assemble five people on a moment's notice, he appointed an executive committee composed of himself, O'Reilly and Pemberton.

It would take countless pages to properly record the work performed by this committee. They were available any time during the day and on any day of the week for conferences pertaining to urgent expressway problems. Their handling of all engineering, legal, right of way and administrative matters was performed in a manner such as only could be done by men of integrity and exceptional business ability.

The second round of posies also should include those who designed, supervised and built the complex system of roads and bridges.

Reynolds, Smith and Hills, architects and engineers, the designers, were well represented by P.M. Huddleston and Harold Aiken whose expertise and judgment were always available to the authority.

The full cooperation of the engineers representing the Florida State Road Department was a most important contribution in keeping the construction work on schedule. Thanks should be extended to the office of the District Engineer, J.A. Brewer in Lake City for his daily participation involving construction. And many thanks should go to A.C. Church, A.L. West, Charles Hopkins, C.D. Dunlap, Malcolm Yancey and J.A. Conner, all excellent engineers with the S.R.D. Tallahassee office for their real interest and help in moving all projects to a successful conclusion.

Cecil C. Bailey, a member of the firm of Rogers, Towers, & Bailey was the general solicitor for the authority and his adept handling and overseeing of all legal matters was always of the highest level.

The authority's right of way department was under the leadership of Richard L. Stanly. He was ably assisted by W. Howard Belote, Thomas Wright, Charles Thomas, William Bockledge, Jack Moore and Vincent Akra.

A most competent group of right of way attorneys was headed by George C. Young, coordinator and expediter, John S. Duss III, David W. Foerster, Harry B. Fozzard, C. Ray Greene Jr., Edward S. Hemphill, Edward P. Mulcahy, Philip N. Selber, and George E. Turner.

The total number of parcels acquired was 2,594 at a cost of $22,723,502 of which only 9.75 per cent were obtained by jury trial.

And last but not least, the contractors performed well on all of their respective jobs, particularly Duval Engineering & Contracting Company, a local firm. Its officers, president George H. Hodges Sr. and Alexander Brest, secretary-treasurer as long time residents of Duval County took personal pride in the quality of their company's construction accomplishments.

A new administration took over the reins of state government in January of 1961 after the inauguration of Farris Bryant as governor and a few weeks later the resignations of Buck and O'Reilly as authority members were accepted by the new governor. The tendered resignation of Pemberton was not accepted at this time.

THE PROPOSED 20TH STREET BRIDGE

Joseph P. Crain, staff writer for *The Florida Times-Union* in his Wednesday, April 20, 1960 report of a meeting of the Jacksonville Expressway Authority held the previous day expressed the thinking of the authority in the following manner:

James H. O'Reilly, authority member, applied the impetus to the new bridge plan with a motion that the authority's engineers immediately begin preliminary studies with the authority's bond underwriters in regard to plans for financing "one or more new bridges across the St. Johns River and other projects."

O'Reilly did not amplify the language of his motion, which was approved unanimously. Authority members at previous sessions have discussed the need for another St. Johns River span beginning somewhere between 8th and 20th streets and connecting with the expressway links tied in with U.S. 1 and U.S. 17.

The authority pinpointed the location of another span across the river at its Tuesday, June 22, 1960 regular meeting when it authorized its financial advisers, engineers and attorney to determine the feasibility of a new bridge across the St. Johns River in the vicinity of 20th Street, a new expressway link through Arlington north of Jacksonville University to Atlantic Boulevard, and an upgrading of the existing expressway through Southside Estates to Greenland and Philips Highway.

Those named to conduct the various phases of the feasibility studies were:

Smith, Barney and Co., New York investment firm who acted as underwriters for the $70 million Expressway Authority bond issue, to act as financial advisers in the matter of additional bond issues to finance the proposed new projects.

Coverdale and Colpitts, New York engineering firm, to act as traffic engineers to determine the traffic and revenue potentials of the new links.

Cecil C. Bailey, local attorney now employed as solicitor for the authority, to act as legal counsel with respect to any new financing and the validation of any additional bonds which may be issued.

Reynolds, Smith and Hills, consulting engineers on the present expressway system as consultant engineers on the proposed new projects.

The U.S. Corps of Engineers publicized through the news media on August 10, 1960 that they had received an application from the Jacksonville Expressway Authority, through Reynolds, Smith and Hills, for approval of preliminary plans for constructing the bridge.

The *Jacksonville Journal* in its Saturday, August 20, 1960 edition editorialized on the application as follows:

The announcement that a public hearing will be held Sept. 13th on the Expressway Authority applications to build a new bridge across the St. Johns River near 20th Street, gives interested citizens time to prepare themselves to make their opinions known regarding the project.

At present, there seems to be a good deal of evidence, at least on the surface, to support those who advocate the need for such a bridge. The growth of Arlington and other suburbs on the east side of the river, and of industry on the west side, suggests that such a bridge would attract considerable patronage. But, whatever is said either for or against the bridge at this early stage, amounts in large part to superficial speculation. A new bridge, costing many millions of dollars, will require considerable planning based on careful forecasts and studies of potential use.

The hearing on September 13th will be concerned primarily with the effect the new bridge would have on navigation, and is seen as a routine meeting. Nevertheless, it will give those who have strong feelings one way or another in the matter the opportunity to air their views.

The Corps of Engineers has invited representatives particularly from navigation interests, city and county officials, and any commercial, industrial or civic groups whose interests may be affected, to attend the hearing. Those who come under this heading should make it their business to attend, bringing with them any evidence or data that may support their views.

The proposed 20th Street Bridge made the headlines in the Wednesday, September 7, 1960 *Jacksonville Journal* in the following manner.

"County Frowns on Another Toll Bridge"

Plans by the Jacksonville Expressway Authority to erect a toll bridge across the St. Johns River at 20th Street are being met with disfavor by the County Commission.

County Engineer John H. Crosby said yesterday that the public already is saturated with toll roads and bridges and resistance is growing daily.

To offset the addition of another toll bridge, the County Commission proposed a route swinging easterly from Main Street and crossing the river via a free bridge near Blount Island.

Survey crews have been given the go-ahead, but Crosby said it would take several months to prepare the necessary documents for acquiring right of way for the proposed road.

Crosby said that the county's proposed road would serve not only the proposed Blount Island industrial project, but also a much greater area of the community by expediting traffic around Jacksovnille's congested area.

Included in the county's plans is the construction of a spur bridge to Blount Island, which would cost about $600,000. The entire Blount Island industrialization project has been delayed by a court suit involving an ownership claim of part of the island.

"Free Bridge Wishful Thinking"

Lucius Buck, Jacksonville Expressway Authority chairman, said yesterday a proposed toll-free bridge across the St. Johns River near Blount Island is wishful thinking.

Earlier this week, the Duval County Commission had discussed a proposal for a southbound route swinging easterly from Main Street north of the city, crossing the river near Blount Island and meeting U.S. Alternate 1 in Arlington.

Buck said yesterday the bridge would cost about $14 million. Neither the county nor the state have any known funds for such an undertaking. The free bridge would divert traffic away from the expressway's toll Trout River and Warren bridges.

The George Washington Hotel was the scene of a meeting called by the U.S. Corps of Engineers on Tuesday, September 13, 1960 to consider the application of the Jacksonville Expressway Authority for the construction of the proposed 20th Street Bridge, over the St. Johns River.

Colonel J.V. Sollohub, who presided at the meeting, explained that it was strictly a fact finding session and a final decision on the application would be made by the office of the secretary of the Army in Washington.

Those opposing the proposed span were:

1.   City Commissioner J. Dillon Kennedy, in charge of municipal docks who stated he was supported by the City Commission in his contention the proposed bridge would hamper the movement of ships to the tanker berth and general cargo berth on Piers 1 and 2.

2.   Captain Jefferson Carey, Captian Vernon Davis and Captain T.R. Priddy, of the St. Johns Bar Pilots Association, also opposed the move. The pilots said that the bridge, if constructed as planned would block half of the available anchorage in the harbor and make the remaining half only partially effective. Carey stated the bridge traffic would create a serious fire hazard to a loaded tanker if burning cigarettes or cigars were tossed from the span to the ship's decks.

3.   Captains W.F. Henson and Phillip Cannon, of Florida Towing Corporation, reviewed the difficulty which the bridge would place in the way of maneuvering vessels to the municipal docks and terminals of Sun Oil and Standard Oil terminal facilities.

4.   Warren B. Jackson, superintendent of the American Oil Company terminal, read a protest from the American Merchant Marine Institute which represented all oil companies operating in and out of the port of Jacksonville.

5.   Floyd Cagle, president of the Propeller Club, stated that the Propeller Club was opposed to the bridge plans as presented.

P.M. Huddleston, representing Reynolds, Smith and Hills, presented plans for the bridge. He said the Expressway Authority was aware of the navigation problems and would seek a satisfactory solution.

Both of the daily newspapers made similar observations on the hearing, one stating "there was no rebuttal to testimony the bridge would hamper navigation" and the other reporting "none of the some 30 persons present at the hearing spoke in favor of the planned location."

A decision of the authority and its engineers to shift the location of the proposed 20th Street Bridge some 400 feet north of the originally proposed location on the west side of the St. Johns River was revealed by J. Dillon Kennedy, utilities commissioner at a meeting of the City Commision held September 20, 1960. He said the new location would not affect the operations of the municipal docks and terminals. As a result of this statement, by resolution, the commission informed the Corps of Engineers that the city would withdraw its objections to the span.

Harold V. Aiken of Reynolds, Smith and Hills, said the proposed change in the plans probably would not overcome the objections filed against the original plans by bar pilots and shipping interests.

Jimmie Walker, staff writer for the *Jacksonville Journal* writing in the October 6, 1960 issue quoted Lucius A. Buck, chairman of the authority, in a long distance telephone report from New York City as saying they had no final decision from bankers on whether the new St. Johns River Bridge and expressway to the Beaches could be financed at this time but at this stage the situation was encouraging. He also said "some questions had not been resolved—among them the cost of design."

Joseph P. Crain, *Florida Times-Union* staff writer, wrote in the November 16, 1960 issue as follows:

"Early construction of a bridge across the St. Johns River in the vicinity of 20th Street and the extension of the Jacksonville expressway system to the Beaches was approved unanimously yesterday."

Acting immediately upon receipt of a favorable financial feasibility report submitted by Cheever Hardwick, representing the New York investment firm of Smith, Barney and Co., the authority set target dates of April 1, 1961 for the sale of the new $39.6 million bond issue and three years for completion of the extension.

Plans for the extension were outlined by P.M. Huddleston, of Reynolds, Smith and Hills, which had completed a cost study of the project.

The bridge and extension would cost $32,728,581, including right of way and other incidental costs, Huddleston said.

Projecting the funding potentials, Hardwick said the traffic studies indicated that the 20th Street span tolls should be the same as that charged on the other expressway bridges—15 cents for an automobile—while commuter tickets would be sold for 10 cents each to users of the new bridge planned to cross the Intracoastal Waterway.

He said the county would have to pledge the gas tax for the retirement of the new bonds, as well as the old, as an "added security" to make the new bonds more attractive to buyers.

The decision of the authority to proceed with the extension was made in a six-point resolution unanimously adopted, which authorized the program and its presentation to the Duval Board of County Commissioners, the State Road Department, the governor and the governor-elect.

"Bridge Site Ruled Out—Plans for New Bridge Rejected." These were the big headlines in the Wednesday, November 23rd and Thursday, November 24th, 1960 editions of the *Jacksonville Journal* and *The Florida Times-Union*.

Both newspapers reported that the U.S. Corps of Engineers had denied the Expressway Authority permission to erect a new bridge across the St. Johns River at 20th Street on the grounds it would "create a distinct hazard to vessel traffic now using the port and would restrict future development thereof." Elaborating, Colonel Sollohub said "the proposed bridge would pass over the only area available in the river for anchorage and turning of deep draft ships. Colonel Sollohub concluded his report with the statement that "he realized it would be a disappointment to the authority and perhaps to the general public here." He also said, "But it is the obligation of the Corps of Engineers to protect the reasonable need of navigation and to insure that the great assets of the port to the community and to the nation are not jeopardized. It is my hope that the Expressway Authority will be able to select another site which can be approved."

Lucius A. Buck, authority chairman, declared: "We've had shockers before, but we've always managed to overcome them and go ahead with our expressway plans. We certainly are not giving up now." He further said he would begin conferences with engineers and counsel to determine what steps the authority should take.

Joseph P. Crain, writing a feature story in the Saturday, December 10, 1960 *Florida Times-Union* made these most significant observations:

> The authority's immediate plans for the future— the new St. Johns
> River Bridge and an extension of the expressway to the Beaches— has
> been stymied by the U.S. Army Corps of Engineers, rejection of the
> bridge plans. But this setback is being explored by the authority and its

engineers, and an answer and an alternate plan are expected to be found soon.

Future specific planning also perhaps will wait upon the results of a $150,000 survey now being made jointly by the County and State Road Department, expected to be finished in about a year, and which is designed to show the areas of the county's future residential and business growth and development and what traffic arteries will be needed to serve them.

Still more St. Johns River spannings will become urgent in the future, even if the projected 20th Street Bridge is constructed.

Discussed has been a crossing just south of the Jacksonville Naval Air Station, which would be a link in a belt route skirting the westerly fringe of the county and after crossing the river, cut northeasterly through the Southside to an ultimate Mayport destination.

Another rapidly approaching need is a new Southside expressway, authority members think— a startling thought with the concrete hardly dry on the present one.

Now, authority members realize, the Mathews and Warren bridges are carrying practically capacity loads during rush hours. And Atlantic Boulevard, east of the Southside expressway is carrying cars bumper-to-bumper in the morning and evening.

Those bridges can't continue to carry traffic increasing at that rate— and there is no indication that the rate will decrease.

The solution may be another expressway cutting across Beach Boulevard and Atlantic Boulevard, to trap much of the increasing traffic and carrying it into downtown Jacksonville over a new bridge crossing from the foot of Haines Street to a point east of the Southside generating station.

The Expressway Authority has demonstrated amply that it has the stature, the economic soundness and the planning ability to meet Jacksonville's current needs. There is no reason to doubt that it will come up with the solutions of this area's booming traffic difficulties of the future.

Time ran out for the fulfillment of any other plans by the original members of the Expressway Authority to build another bridge spanning the St. Johns River for as stated in the previous chapter, the resignations of Chairman Lucius A. Buck and Secretary James H. O'Reilly were accepted by Governor Farris Bryant on January 6, 1961.

CHAPTER XXI

THE 1963 REVENUE BOND PROGRAM

The everyday commuter, the occasional rider and every visitor who travels the Isaiah D. Hart Expressway-Bridge facilities, have one thing in common in that they express openly and enthusiastically their appreciation of the magnificent structure as a thing of beauty and utility.

They know that within minutes they can move from bustling downtown Jacksonville to their own select places of rest and serenity. But they don't know what transpired behind the scenes that culminated in the building of such a graceful and eye-pleasing transportation complex.

As most people are curious, particularly about their acquaintances, friends and those persons whose public and private pronouncements might affect their daily lives, it might be revealing to know what transpired before the 1963 revenue bond issue program finally became a reality.

New faces and personalities took over the responsibilities of the Jacksonville Expressway Authority in 1961.

After accepting the resignations of Buck and O'Reilly, Governor Farris Bryant on January 10th named banker Roger L. Main as chairman and businessman Frederick H. Schultz to serve the unexpired terms.

The governor said he was confident that Main, president and chairman of the board of directors of the Florida National Bank in Jacksonville, and Schultz would "bring to the expressway a new vigor and a determination for progress which will expedite construction of a new bridge across the St. Johns."

In accepting the honor Main said, "I am honored that Governor Bryant has selected me for this important post. In accepting it, I assure the citizens of Jacksonville and Duval County that I am vitally aware of the importance of the work of the expressway to the development of our entire area. I plan to devote much of my time to the work of the authority and to justify the responsibility which the governor has placed upon me."

On January 17th the authority held its first meeting since reorganization.

Main introduced himself and the three other new members of the authority— Schultz, Ralph Powers, also a member of the State Road Board and Fletcher Morgan, County Commission Board chairman— to an audience which included former Chairman Buck.

Main said the former members under Buck's leadership had accomplished wonders during their term in office.

Buck replied that he was "delighted to see that the governor appointed men of integrity and ability to the authority."

No major policy matters were considered by the authority other than the selection of Frederick Schultz to serve as its secretary.

Within a matter of a few weeks the new authority chairman and members were apprised by the executive director of the immediate past history of the expressway program and pending problems. Of particular interest to the authority was the transportation study made in 1960 by the Florida State Road Department in cooperation with the U.S. Bureau of Public Roads and the Board of County Commissioners, who contributed $60,000 toward making the study.

Although the official findings of the study had not been put in final form, it was known that conclusions had been reached and the Road Department was in a position to give this information to any interested local governmental agency.

Accordingly, at 11:00 A.M. on February 22, 1961, M.A. Conner, engineer of traffic and planning, Florida State Road Department, his assistant Edward Mueller and J.A. Brewer, district engineer, S.R.D. met with members of the authority and the authority's executive director.

Conner and Mueller gave a detailed account of the department's traffic survey which included recommendations for the construction of future bridges across the St. Johns River in the vicinity of 8th Street, Commodore Point and just south of the Jacksonville Naval Station. Charts were shown indicating travel corridors and the needs for improving feeder roads. Conner said a bridge at Commodore Point should be built first and the next one constructed in the area around 8th Street.

Mr. Conner further informed the authority that due to the magnitude of the report and the necessity of completing charts, maps and drawings for printing purposes, it would be at least a year or more before printed copies of the transportation study would be available for public distribution.

On February 25, 1961, Edward Wemple, representing Coverdale and Colpitts, Traffic Engineers of N.Y., met informally with Chairman Main, authority member Schultz, Arthur Sollee the authority executive director, David W. Foerster general counsel for the authority, P.M. Huddleston, representing Reynolds, Smith and Hills, and Charles W. Johnson, Jr., certified public accountant for the authority. They discussed the needs for additional traffic feasibility studies for bridges at Commodore Point and south of the Jacksonville Naval Air Station.

It was suggested that Reynolds, Smith and Hills proceed with location plans for a Commodore Point Expressway-Bridge project and Coverdale and Colpitts review existing data and then give the authority estimates on a new origin and destination survey.

A feasibility study of further extensions to the expressway system including another bridge across the St. Johns River was officially authorized by the authority on March 21, 1961 and Chairman Main also was empowered to enter into a contract with Coverdale and Colpitts, for a potential earnings survey of a new bridge across the St. Johns River at a location other than the earlier proposed 20th Street site rejected by the Army engineers.

During the following months in 1961, numerous informal meetings were held to discuss the many problems that would have to be resolved prior to taking action. The most important of these were:

Monday, May 8th: Mr. Wemple, of Coverdale and Colpitts, met with Main, Schultz, General Counsel Foerster and the executive director to discuss traffic surveys being made. Wemple reviewed personnel requirements for the Origin and Destination Study and requested State Road Department cooperation.

On May 23rd a conference was held at the U.S. engineer's office to informally discuss the proposed location of a bridge from Commodore Point to the Southside near Highland Avenue. Among those present were: Colonel Sollohub and McKnight, U.S. engineers office; Messrs. Main, Schultz, Foerster and the executive director for the Jacksonville Expressway Authority; Messrs. Brown, Carey and Davis, St. Johns River bar pilots; Sam Marshall representing Commodore Point Terminal Company and others.

Mr. Huddleston of Reynolds, Smith and Hills, consulting engineers, outlined the location of the proposed bridge which was immediately rejected by the pilots and other shipping interests as being equally as bad as the rejected 20th Street Bridge location.

Tuesday, June 6th: Main and the executive director met with Mr. Huddleston of Reynolds, Smith and Hills, and suggested a new location for the Commodore Point Bridge to overcome objections by navigation interests.

Thursday, June 15th: Mr. Wemple of Coverdale and Colpitts gave a preliminary traffic report and Huddleston presented a new alignment for a bridge at Commodore Point.

Robert Dunivan, of the S.R.D. gave a brief report on the findings and conclusions of the state's traffic study of Duval County.

Wednesday, June 21st: In order to get the advice of the bar pilots a conference was arranged for authority member Schultz, the authority attorney Foerster and the executive director to meet with bar pilots Davis, Reese, Carey and Phillips and W.T. Coppedge, Sr. representing tugboat owners.

The detailed location of the bridge which had been worked out by the authority's executive director took into consideration the tides, currents, location of main river piers, vertical and horizontal clearances and channel lights. After an examination of the map and being informed of the navigational features, the bar pilots agreed the proposed bridge from Commodore Point to the Southside, if constructed and located as outlined, would not be objectionable. They said the channel span lights would be of great assistance to them in moving ships around the bend in the river.

The last six months of 1961 were devoted to studying financial feasibility reports, traffic reports, engineering costs and the possibility of receiving Bureau of Public Roads approval of the proposed Commodore Point Bridge project as an integral part of a proposed easterly interstate bypass route.

At the authority December meeting, Chairman Main pledged the authority's cooperation with other public bodies to help meet the road needs of Duval County.

The authority during the early months of 1962 spent countless hours with its consulting engineers, traffic engineer and financial advisers in order to determine if it were feasible to finance projects based upon engineering estimates of revenues and costs.

After getting assurances that it was feasible to finance certain bridge and expressway projects, the authority arranged for a conference with the County Commission on April 17th in the office of Reynolds, Smith and Hills. A preliminary plan of construction and financing was suggested to the commission which required a pledge by the county of gas tax monies as further security for bonds necessary to finance the project.

This plan was turned down emphatically by the county.

Undaunted by the attitude of the County Commission, the authority publicly presented its plans on May 30th for the construction of additional bridges across the St. Johns River which would be served by expressway approaches. The proposed method of financing the projects was explained in detail by a member of a prominent banking firm from New York City.

The expressway expansion program was again presented by the authority to the County Commission on June 26th. As in the first conference the authority's proposal was again rejected.

July provided a field day for the news media for statements made by the County Commission, Jacksonville City Commission and Council were given big headlines whenever pronouncements or blasts were directed at the Jacksonville Expressway Authority.

It appeared these political bodies were determined to make it a long hot summer for the authority for during this period, a baker's dozen of salvos were fired at the authority, eliciting newspaper headlines such as:

"Duval Commission Comes out Against Expressway Plans."
"Meeting Sought by City on Plan for Expressway."
"Says Bonds Unnecessary."
"'Busy Main' Delays Road Meet with City."

"Toll Cut Asked by Commission."

"Expressway Officials Draw Fire of City."

"County Board Opposes Plan for Belt Road."

"Harris Asks: Why New Expressway Plan?"

"Expressway Perils Roads, Harris Says."

"Expressway Expansion Battle Still a Toss-up."

"Greene Lambastes Expressway Plan."

"City Council Straddles Expressway Fence."

"Citizens Body to Study Expressway Expansion."

Adding a peculiar twist to the county's thinking was the July appointment of a Citizens Expressway Advisory Committee, charged with studying the expansion proposal and reporting back to the County Commission. Named were Lucius A. Buck, former chairman of the Jacksonville Expressway Authority to serve as committee chairman, Chalmers D. Horne, E. Robert Langley, Daniel A. Naughton and Lester Sanders.

The authority took the harassment and sniping in stride and calmly continued to be receptive to suggestions by the County Commission on ways to finalize a highway program that would best meet and serve the needs of the traveling public with the limited funds available.

This cooperative and reasonable attitude finally began to show results. Leaked information to the authority indicated the County Commission had contacted Ralph Powers, a member of both the authority and State Road Board and James Kynes, administrative assistant to Governor Farris Bryant, relative to the inclusion of certain county, state and federal roads as feeder roads in the proposed expressway expansion plans of the authority.

On October 4th in the office of W.C. Drenning, construction coordinator for the authority, J.S. Ward, district engineer, S.R.D, Lake City, Florida, presented a list of proposed feeder roads to Drenning, Sollee, the executive director for the authority and W. Littlefield, representing Sverdrup & Parcel and Associates, Inc., the authority's consulting engineers, successor to Reynolds, Smith and Hills.

The Chronicle, a local weekly newspaper, during the next few weeks printed stories that S.R.D. engineers were in Duval County to expedite preliminary work on more than 70 miles of highway and that top aides of Governor Bryant had been in conference with the County Commission.

The Jacksonville Civic Auditorium was the focal point for the Expressway Authority on Thursday morning October 25th as the U.S. Corps of Engineers held a public hearing on the application of the authority for a high level bridge across the St. Johns River from Commodore Point to the Southside near Highland Avenue.

Unlike the hearing on the rejected 20th Street span, the Bar Pilots Association representative, T.R. Priddy, said he did not believe the proposed Commodore Point span would interfere with navigation.

Another speaker, Sam Marshall, representing the Commodore Point Terminal Corporation, whose company would be overpassed by the proposed bridge stated that the proposal would not affect them too much.

In all, some 60 persons attended the hearing and only one of them expressed any dissatisfaction with the proposed location or with the preliminary plans for the structure.

The Florida Times-Union, the day following the public hearing, quoted County Commissioner Bob Harris as saying the County Commission would agree with the Expressway Authority's request for a pledge of county secondary road funds to back the pending expressway bond issue, provided the authority would sell enough additional bonds so that $25 million would be available for the construction of the county's secondary road improvement program.

Harris said Ralph Powers of Lake City, State Road Board member for the 2nd District, had reviewed the proposal and had agreed the $25 million program "would be the greatest road program any county has every attempted."

Harris also said he wanted to thank the advisory committee appointed by the County Commission for its efforts, and promptly dismissed the committee.

The afternoon *Journal* quoted Ralph Powers as saying "primary road funds for Duval County would not be affected by the bond financing." This same article by Bill Sweisgood stated, "There were some rumblings over the fact that some of the roads that Harris planned to have improved with the bond issue financed by expressway bridge tolls are primary roads— improvements of which is a state responsibility."

Big headlines greeted the early risers on Monday, October 29th with "Buck Quits Citizens Expressway Group— Harris Bond Plan Comes Under Fire."

Pertinent quotations from Buck's letter to Harris, dated October 27, said:

> When you called me early this week concerning the report of the advisory committee, I told you that we were nearing the end of our work and the submission of a report. You then indicated your continuing interest in the work of the committee and stated that you did not wish to rush us. Your statement of yesterday without any previous advice to your committee is hardly consistent with your assurances.

> Personally I want to disassociate myself from your plan.

> The building and improvement of state roads in the county is supposed to be done by the state, out of revenues available for that purpose and not out of tolls or out of the county's gas tax.

Surely there is a duty to the people of the county to devise a more realistic, less dangerous and less expensive program. A reckless and hurried pursuit of this program is not progress.

A meeting of the minds between the expressway Authority and the Board of County Commissioners was much in the news during the last days of October. At its meeting of the 29th, the authority ratified a proposal by the commission that a $25 million county secondary road improvement program be added to the authority's plans for a $54 million expansion of the expressway system. On the 31st the County Commission formally repledged the County's share of state gasoline tax as added security for Expressway Authority bonds that would finance both programs.

The authority held its regular meeting on November 14th when it received from the County Commission its resolution of October 31 pledging gasoline tax for the issuance of $152 million in bonds.

Chairman Main, attorney David W. Foerster and bond attorney Frank Watson went to Miami on December 6th for a conference with representatives from the Bureau of Public Roads, Witten, Turner, Call and Anderson and S.R.D. representatives Ralph Powers, Mayo and Charles Hopkins to see if the bureau would agree with the authority to construct a toll bridge across the St. Johns River just south of the Jacksonville Naval Air Station to the Mandarin area. This the bureau refused to do.

The status of the proposed South County Line Bridge was partly revealed by Governor Farris Bryant on March 7, 1963 when he told Duval County officials that the state was waiting for a decision on whether it would be a free or toll bridge.

The question was put to rest by an announcement from Governor Bryant on April 3, that the South County Line Bridge would be constructed by the Bureau of Public Roads as part of Interstate 295 and as a free facility.

At the same time Main stated the proposed bond issue would be reduced by $16 million.

The County Commission submitted their secondary roads improvement program to Coverdale and Colpitts, for their review and recommendations.

On May 2, 1963 a conference was held in the authority's office to discuss their findings. Those present were County Commissioners Bob Harris and Julian Warren; County Engineer John Crosby; Authority Chairman Roger L. Main; and members Charles Hoffman, Walter Cowart, and Ralph Powers, also a member of the State Road Board; S.R.D. Engineers Jim Brewer and J.D. Ward; Winston Littlefield representing Sverdrup & Parcel and Associates, Inc., authority consulting engineers; Gene Rees of the engineering firm of Beiswenger and Hoch; the Authority's Executive Director Arthur N. Sollee and Edward Wemple representing the traffic engineers.

Wemple reviewed each county suggested feeder road in great detail. He cited those roads or parts of roads that would meet the requirements and criteria and those that failed to meet the qualifications.

Wemple later submitted an order of priority on the importance of construction schedule for those qualified roads, a list at considerable variance with the one suggested by the commission.

Even though engineering studies and preliminary design work were well on their way, the ultimate success of the entire expressway program depended upon the sale of revenue bonds.

After the completion of all fiscal, engineering and legal work the attorneys for the authority filed for validation its proposed $140 million expressway bond issue in the local court on July 24, 1963.

J.C. Green, *Times-Union* staff writer, reporting in the July 26th edition stated:

Circuit Court Judge William L. Durden yesterday set a double-purpose hearing for 3 p.m. next Wednesday on two suits which ultimately will decide the fate of a proposed $140 million bond issue to finance expansion of the Jacksonville Expressway improvements to some of its major feeder roads.

One of the suits is a petition by the authority asking circuit court to validate the bonds. The petition was filed Wednesday morning just a few minutes after the Board of County Commissioners had repledged the county's share of state gas taxes as added security for the bonds in case revenues from expressway toll bridges are not sufficient to retire the issue.

The other suit is a complaint by a private citizen and taxpayer, Leon Anderson, asking the court to enjoin issuance of the bonds.

It was filed for Anderson during the previous February by Attorney William D. Barfield.

After a series of legal maneuvering a hearing was finally held before Judge Durden.

Shortly thereafter, on October 11th, he approved the bond issue stating he was holding that the Expressway Authority complied with all legal requirements in preparing the bond issue.

The next hurdle to be overcome was the Florida Supreme Court, for the State Bond Review Board had already approved the proposed bond issue on August 27th.

The Expressway Authority's proposed bond issue was argued before the Supreme Court in Tallahassee on December 9th. The authority was ably represented by Jones and Foerster, the authority's attorneys, the opposition by assistant State Attorney Frank M. Scruby for the state of Florida, by attorney William Barfield representing Leon Anderson, a taxpayer. Both Scruby and Barfield urged the court to reverse the October order of Duval Circuit Court Judge William Durden which validated the bonds for sale.

The court took the case under advisement.

Although the authority had hoped for an early ruling by the Supreme Court it was not until February 5, 1964 that the high court, in an opinion written by retired Justice T. Frank Hobson, declared the bond issue "desirable and proper, in the best interest of the authority, Duval County and its citizens— definitely a public purpose and the purpose for which the authority was created."

The authority immediately set a timetable for future developments which unfolded as follows:

Received and accepted a bid on its $135 million bond issue of 4.1162 percent on March 12th, which amount was $5 million less than the original proposed bond issue.

In New York City, on April 1st received a check for $135 million as payment for the expressway revenue bonds.

Instructed its engineers to work at full speed in order that the completion date of the Commodore Point project as set forth in the official statement would be met.

The meeting of the authority held on April 10, 1964 was uniquely different from previous meetings. On this date there were no "ifs" and "ands" as to the validation of bonds or the sale of bonds. Money was available and being invested in government securities until actually needed— the program was on its way.

The seemingly routine meeting did not reveal the undercurrent of satisfaction that was felt by each authority member and the entire staff for past accomplishments— nor was it outwardly indicated that bigger jobs lay ahead: the job of acquiring rights of way, the job of designing the roads and bridges and the ultimate— the job of building highways and structures on time and on schedule.

The job of obtaining all of the rights of way was the task of the right of way section. It was headed by a most competent Richard L. Stanly. His two very valuable and knowledgeable assistants were Howard Belote and Thomas Wright.

The authority employed the most qualified appraisers, all of whom were capable of defending their work in the courts, if it became necessary. Such men were J. Alvin Register, Jr., Richard Hamilton, Roy F. Smith, Jr., Frank K. Osborn and Stewart B. Steeg.

Monetary matters were supervised by C. Moody Cullum, comptroller, whose outstanding ability in the field of finance was recognized by the country's leading financial institutions.

David W. Foerster was the general counsel for the authority and his four years of extraordinary service fully justified his selection. His brilliant and thorough handling of all rights of way condemnation suits saved the authority hundreds of thousands of dollars.

The entire 1963 bond program required the acquisition of 537 parcels at a cost of $7,295,000.

The consulting engineers for the authority, Sverdrup and Parcel and Associates, were represented by Winn Littlefield, their regional vice president, Jim Gast, vice president, Jack Dent, Frank House, and Ed Bunnell engineering supervisor of all construction work. It was Mr. Bunnell's insistence on excellent work and jobs being completed on time that was a major factor in the completion of the bond program on time. Both Mr. Littlefield and Mr. Gast were highly respected for their efficient and clear presentations of all engineering matters.

Active assistance was received from the engineers of the Florida State Road Department. Special thanks should be extended to J.D. Ward, district engineer, Lake City and to M.A. Connar, C.J. Schenck, P.W. Ekey, Charles Hopkins, C.D. Dunlap and H.W. Overstreet from the S.R.D., Tallahassee office.

Overseeing all of the expressway construction work for the authority was Charles Baldwin a most capable and trustworthy construction coordinator. It was he who kept his finger on the progress of all projects. His devotion to excellence was a contributing factor in obtaining fine workmanship.

It was through the cooperative and team effort of all those connected with the 1963 bond program that the target completion date of November 1, 1967, set on July 1, 1963, was actually met, but due to the inability of Governor Claude Kirk to attend the scheduled opening ceremonies, Authority Chairman Roger L. Main, in his usual and very efficient manner, officially moved the dedicatory opening to the next day, November 2, 1967. At this time the Commodore Point Bridge was officially named the Isaiah D. Hart Bridge.

Jennifer Fewell, daughter of Mr. and Mrs. John Fewell, one of the descendants of Hart, cut the ribbon opening the span.

The 1963 revenue bond issue made it possible to complete the following construction program:

1.   The revenue producing Commodore Point Expressway-Bridge project.

2.   Atlantic Boulevard and Mayport Road project which included a bridge on Atlantic Boulevard over the Intracoastal Waterway and the Atlantic Boulevard-Mayport Road overpass.

3.   Roosevelt Boulevard overpass at Edgewood Avenue project.

4.   System improvements project. This $25 million project was made possible by an allocation by the Jacksonville Expressway Authority from revenue bond funds for the improving of Duval County, state and federal

roads as feeders to the expressway system. The highways improved and reconstructed were: Arlington Road, Cesery Boulevard, Rogero Road, Emerson Street, University Boulevard, Cassat Avenue, Lane Avenue, Blanding Boulevard, Roosevelt Boulevard, Edgewood Avenue, Soutel Drive, Lenox Avenue, Chaffee Road and Moncrief Road.

If any reader is interested in details concerning the 1963 revenue bond issue, then a visit to the offices of the Jacksonville Transportation Authority should be made where the reports of Sverdrup & Parcels and Associates, Inc. Consulting Engineers, are available.

CHAPTER XXII
THE 1963 BOND PROGRAM — IN RETROSPECT

The county's position in the early stages of the 1963 bond program was crystal clear in their insistence that the county road system had deteriorated so badly that at least $25 million was needed to improve secondary roads.

In *The Florida Times-Union* Sunday edition of July 8, 1962 County Commission Chairman Bob Harris was quoted as follows:

Harris called a press conference yesterday to issue a formal written statement which he said had the hearty approval of the entire Board of County Commissioners.

We're not opposed to expansion of the expressway, but with the cooperation of the city and county governments after other needs are cared for, he said in remarks prefacing his reading of the statement.

By other needs, Harris explained he meant the secondary roads in areas of the county outside the various municipalities.

Harris said the county commissioners are presently drafting plans for a comprehensive program to improve the secondary roads.

He said such plans would contemplate resurfacing, widening and extending present paved secondary roads, paving and improving of existing unpaved roads, and building new roads in fast developing suburban areas.

In a luncheon talk before the Arlington Kiwanis Club on July 17, 1962, Harris said a re-pledge of the county's gas tax for a proposed expressway expansion would kill prospects for more than $5.5 million worth of badly needed work on secondary roads in his district.

Later the commission announced that $5 million would be spent for road improvements in each county commissioner's district.

The news media also publicized the county's $25 million road program by enumerating the earmarked projects for each commissioner's district.

The county had vigorously proclaimed the need for improving their own road system, yet the roads listed in their $25 million improvement program were glaringly conspicuous by the inclusion of roads in the state's primary road system, such as Roosevelt Boulevard, State Road No. 15 and U.S. 17; Blanding Boulevard, State Road No. 21; a section of Atlantic Boulevard, State Road No. 10; and Old Kings Road, State Road No. 15.

The county also insisted the authority should build new highways to the Atlantic Beach-Mayport areas or improve Atlantic Boulevard, State Road 10 and Mayport Road, State Road A1A.

The big question was why did the county sponsor the improving of primary state roads with bond money when their original objections to the repledging of the surplus gas tax was that their own road system needed at least $25 million?

This question may never be answered, which leaves the field wide open for speculation. And as speculation and mystery are so closely associated, it is quite possible that inferences and conclusions may be drawn after reading a chronological series of events presented by H. George Carrison, bond consultant, to the Board of County Commissioners of Duval County at the board meeting held on June 8, 1964.

This five page document to the commission covers a period from April 17, 1962 through March 12, 1964 and is intended to justify a fee for services rendered by Carrison as bond consultant to the commission. Some of the events quite apropos are now cited:

April 17, 1962 to April 20, 1962: Attended meeting April 17, held jointly between Jacksonville Expressway Authority and Duval County Commission, at the offices of Reynolds, Smith and Hills. Immediately following joint meeting, a series of conferences began between Commission Chairman, Bob Harris and me to discuss advisability of county pledging gas tax. Also discussed was the potential amount of money the county should demand for construction access roads in consideration of county pledging its gas tax. After conferences endeavor was made by me to convince Expressway Authority of the correctness of county's position regarding access roads, and to the obtaining of an agreement from the authority to include access roads in the forthcoming expressway financing. Expressway Authority refused.

October 25, 1962: At the suggestion of Commissioner Harris, I went to see Commissioner Ray Green at his home and discussed at great length the new idea for expressway financing. I obtained his agreement to support the financing, provided the $25 million for access roads were included.

October 26, 1962: Accompanied Commissioner Harris, Mr. Ray Richardson and County Engineer, John Crosby to Lake City for a detailed discussion of Duval County access road financing, with Road Department member, Mr. Ralph Powers.

October 29, 1962: I advised County Commission to make gas tax pledge in support of Jacksonville Expressway Authority's financing and the commission voted to do so, however the pledge was made covering the total bond issue in excess of my limit of $143 million.

February 15, 1963: Meeting with several commissioners to discuss possible ways of getting help from the Road Department in reducing the total amount of the bond issue by getting it to assume certain capital expenses of the program.

April 4, 1963: Luncheon meeting with full Board of County Commissioners to discuss new developments regarding the expressway and a telephone conversation held among the commissioners, the governor, and James Kynes, the governor's administrative assistant, wherein it was reported that the Road Department would assume the south county bridge construction and that the total bond issue would be reduced to $136 million. This made everyone quite happy and I expressed the opinion that we were now on very sound financial ground.

April 16, 1963: Went to Tallahassee for discussions of the Expressway with Mr. James Kynes.

What influence the state had with the County Commission is pure conjecture but the results show that instead of the county receiving $25 million for the improving of their secondary roads, this amount was considerably reduced, due to approximately $5.7 million being committed to federal and state roads.

The authority likewise, on the Atlantic Boulevard and Mayport Road projects, had spent $5,200,000 on these two state roads plus an additional $1,740,000 on the Roosevelt Boulevard (U.S. 17) overcrossing.

The S.R.D. contributed $1,500,000 toward the construction of the Atlantic Boulevard-Intracoastal Waterway Bridge, which was their total contribution to the 1963 bond issue program undertaken by the authority.

Of the $139 million invested in the existing expressway system, Duval County had contributed $108 million; the state and federal government the difference.

Another unexplained event was the filing of a suit to block the issuance of the authority's proposed revenue bonds, by Leon Anderson, a taxpayer and retired employee of the Navy, who resided at 3537 Laura Street.

What prompted Anderson to expend funds to employ attorney William D. Barfield, to not only file the suit, but to carry the case through the Supreme Court is an interested question.

Mr. Barfield did an admirable job in the local circuit court. In fact, his questions propounded to all of the witnesses for the authority was astoundingly appropriate and uncannily clever. The most remarkable question by Barfield occurred when my deposition was taken before James A. Joseph, notary public, when he asked—"Mr. Sollee, when you were executive director of the authority, prior to January 1, 1961, did you in your official capacity oppose or endorse the 20th Street Bridge?"

Some observers at the trial commented that it appeared Barfield must have been gifted with extrasensory perception so knowledgeable was he about former and existing expressway problems. There also was speculation as to why Messrs. Anderson and Barfield sought so strenuously to delay the program. Intuition suggested Anderson could have been a front for a few well-to-do disgruntled persons who had been very closely affiliated with, and were privy to the workings of the previous authority. Barfield also appeared to have been briefed very thoroughly as to what questions should be brought up and what procedures should be followed.

CHAPTER XXIII
HISTORY OF
J. TURNER BUTLER BOULEVARD

On November 10, 1927, pursuant to a resolution previously adopted by the Board of County Commissioners of Duval County, Florida, the board passed a resolution for order-of-opening of a new road in Duval County, the description approximately being an extension of Hogan Road, County Road No. 14 beginning at Big Pottsburg Creek and extending southeasterly and easterly to a point in the southern end of Jacksonville Beach in the vicinity of the Atlantic Ocean some several hundred feet north of the Duval-St. Johns County line. See Exhibit A for location shown on copy of map dated December 13, 1931.

This alignment for a future new road to the Beaches was still valid up until the time the Florida East Coast Railway Company abandoned, in the early '30's, its use of its tracks that served all the Beaches and Mayport.

After several years of negotiations between the commissioners and the officials of the F.E.C.R.R. the county in 1937 purchased the entire F.E.C. right of way, within the jurisdiction of the county, for the sum of $8,500. Subsequently the idea of a new road to the Beaches via the Hogan Road alignment was placed in the background, for Beach Boulevard was constructed by the Florida State Road Department on the F.E.C.R.R. right of way and the official dedication for the opening of Beach Boulevard was held on December 17, 1949.

A transportation study of the Jacksonville-Duval County Metropolitan Area was initiated by the Duval County Commission through a resolution dated August 24, 1959, in which the State Road Department was requested to conduct the study and the county agreed to finance one-half the cost.

In early 1961 the Jacksonville Expressway Authority was informed that the State Road Department was in a position to make a verbal traffic report covering the Duval County Metropolitan Area.

Accordingly, a conference was held on February 22, 1961 in the offices of the Jacksonville Expressway Authority for a presentation to the authority by the state of their findings and recommendations for future expressway projects. Those present were: M.A. Conner and Ed Mueller, State Road Department, Tallahassee, Florida; Chairman Roger Main, Fred Schultz, secretary and Arthur N. Sollee, executive director, Jacksonville Expressway Authority; and Jim Brewer, district engineer, State Road Department, Lake City, Florida. The state's findings indicated a 20 year growth factor, 1960 to 1980 as 6.04 for the southeast, 6.04 east, 3.74 north, 3.74 northwest, 3.74 west and 3.74 southwest. These figures showed the need for St. Johns River crossings from the Commodore Point area in downtown Jacksonville southeasterly and from the downtown area of Jacksonville easterly somewhere between 8th Street and Union Street to the Arlington area. It was also brought out that by extending the southeast corridor from the Commodore Point Bridge (now Hart Bridge) further southeastward to Southside Boulevard, the immediate need of an east-west crossing would be greatly reduced.

With the above in mind the authority instructed its engineers to make preliminary studies of a proposed St. Johns River crossing at Commodore Point with feeder roads extending to downtown Jacksonville to the west and feeder roads on the south side of the river that would go south and west and also southeast. The preliminary southeasterly section would extend southeasterly with proposed connections to Atlantic Boulevard, University Boulevard, Beach Boulevard near the vicinity of Hogan Road near Patti's Restaurant and an extension further southeasterly parallel and adjacent to Hogan Road with a connection to Southside Boulevard (U.S. Alt. 1). The thinking at that time was, that at some future date a new alignment to the Beaches would generally follow the Old Hogan Road alignment shown on Exhibit A.

Examine Exhibit B and note how simple it would have been to extend the expressway to Southside Boulevard from Beach Boulevard. Green dots indicate the approximate alignment proposed in 1961.

This alignment would have provided a shorter and more direct route to Southside Boulevard. Also it would have eliminated a great amount of traffic on Southside Boulevard originating south of Beach Boulevard and desiring to go west on Beach Boulevard. The left turn movement would have been eliminated.

The question is: Then why did not the authority extend the expressway to Southside Boulevard along the Hogan Road location?

The answer is: On March 27, 1962 an elected county official came to the office of the executive director and told him in no uncertain terms that the Board of County Commissioners would never approve or agree to the extension of the expressway from the vicinity of Hogan Road near Patti's Restaurant along the Hogan Road alignment to Southside Boulevard. He said the reason was this proposed extension would divert quite a bit of traffic from using the Arlington Expressway between Arlington Road and University Boulevard and certain businesses owned by friends of his along the Arlington Expressway would be adversely affected. He further added the county would never agree to repledge the surplus gas tax as added security for a revenue bond issue unless the plan then being considered to extend the expressway to Southside Boulevard along Hogan Road was dropped.

After receiving such a mandate from this county official, whose influence was at a high peak, the authority changed plans so the expressway would start curving only eastward near Patti's Restaurant with off and on ramps being at points in the center of Beach Boulevard and as now existing.

Because at some future date there would be a need for an additional highway from the Beaches area to serve various sections of Duval County, it was obvious that a part of the old proposed Hogan Road alignment would be an ideal location to serve this purpose. Studies indicated that by extending the Hogan Road alignment westerly, ideal connections could be made at U.S. Alternate 1 (Southside Boulevard), Belfort Road, Interstate 95 and Philips Highway. There also was the exciting possibility of further extending this alignment in a westerly direction to form connections at San Jose Boulevard (State Road 13) and continue across the St. Johns River to connect to Roosevelt Boulevard (U.S. 27). This alignment was originally designated as Jose-Vedra Boulevard. See Exhibit C.

The authority and its staff in its never ending process of continuing to think and plan for the future traffic needs for Duval County made public for the first time its thinking in the Sunday, December 27, 1964 centennial edition of *The Florida Times-Union*. Along with several other proposed new routes, an east-west alignment was shown, part of which now constitutes J. Turner Butler Boulevard. The proposed east-west route received extensive news coverage with feature articles as follows: *Times-Union*, Sunday, March 14, 1965; *Journal*, Saturday, March 13, 1965; *Times-Union*, Sunday, July 25, 1965; Wednesday, March 29, 1967; Saturday, August 17, 1968; Tuesday, October 1, 1968 and Thursday, November 14, 1968.

With the above future plan in mind, several owners of large tracts of land along the original Hogan Road alignment were contacted and asked if they would donate a 200-foot right of way for a limited access highway that might be built in the distant future. Such contacts had been started in 1963 and continued intermittently until the summer of 1967. At this time some of the owners said they would give the right of way if an adjacent owner would do the same. The impasse was broken when a group of owners of one tract said they would give the right of way but the deed would be withheld until other deeds were received by the Jacksonville Expressway Authority.

During all of these talks, the need had been stressed for a limited access highway where safety would be a paramount factor. This position was made known to the attorneys representing the owners.

During several conferences, I was informed the owners would not give an outright limited access deed but would give one incorporating limited access and controlled access features. The reasons given were as follows:

1. In the 1950 bond issue construction program, the State Road Department built a service road on the east side of the Haines Street expressway, north of the Gator Bowl interchange to the railroad tracks just south of Haines Street.

2. In this same construction program the State Road Department built service roads on both sides of Southside Boulevard, a designated limited access highway, between Atlantic Boulevard and Beach Boulevard. Also on the west side of Southside Boulevard a service road was built from Beach Boulevard south to a point just south of Hogan Road.

3.   On Southside Boulevard every permit issued by the State Road Department for a direct connection from adjacent property to the main expressway was only valid until such time as a service road was constructed. Then access would be only to the service road. Based upon this wording, it was evident the State Road Department contemplated building service roads on both sides of Southside Boulevard.

4.   The Jacksonville Expressway Authority had already constructed service roads on both sides of the Arlington expressway.

5.   The Jacksonville Expressway Authority was in the process of constructing service roads on the west and east sides of the Haines Street expressway.

6.   To insist that a limited access right of way be given without adequate access would not be in accordance with the track record of the State Road Department and Jacksonville Expressway Authority.

7.   The interstate system of defense highways with its strict limited access features was designed to move traffic through, around and from city to city and state to state.

8.   The local expressway system is primarily for the convenience of Duval County citizens with through traffic an incidental adjunct. Also as the expressway system is local in character the burden for paying for it is a Duval County problem. This being the case, due consideration should be given to constructing the various elements of the system so that it will induce, serve and attract the greatest possible number of toll-paying vehicles. It has been demonstrated that good and adequate feeder roads are essential contributing revenue projects. An example is the 20th Street expressway which was constructed as a contributing revenue project.

In view of the above preponderance of evidence, deeds were accepted from several owners for a 200-foot right of way, incorporating controlled and limited access features subject to certain provisions.

At this time it should be noted that the State Department of Transportation had completed a two-way service road on the west side of Southside Boulevard, north from Baymeadows Road for a distance approximating 1.5 miles.

Also, a Southside Boulevard extension study by the Florida Department of Transportation includes plans for the construction of one-way service roads on both sides of the boulevard from the vicinity of the Arlington triangle south to the connection to Interstate 95.

It may be of some interest to know that on January 9, 1969 the authority approved construction of a highway east of Southside Boulevard (U.S. Alternate 1) to a university site, provided the site was first selected for a university. Roger L. Main, authority chairman, in a letter to Gert H.W. Schmidt, chairman of Mayor

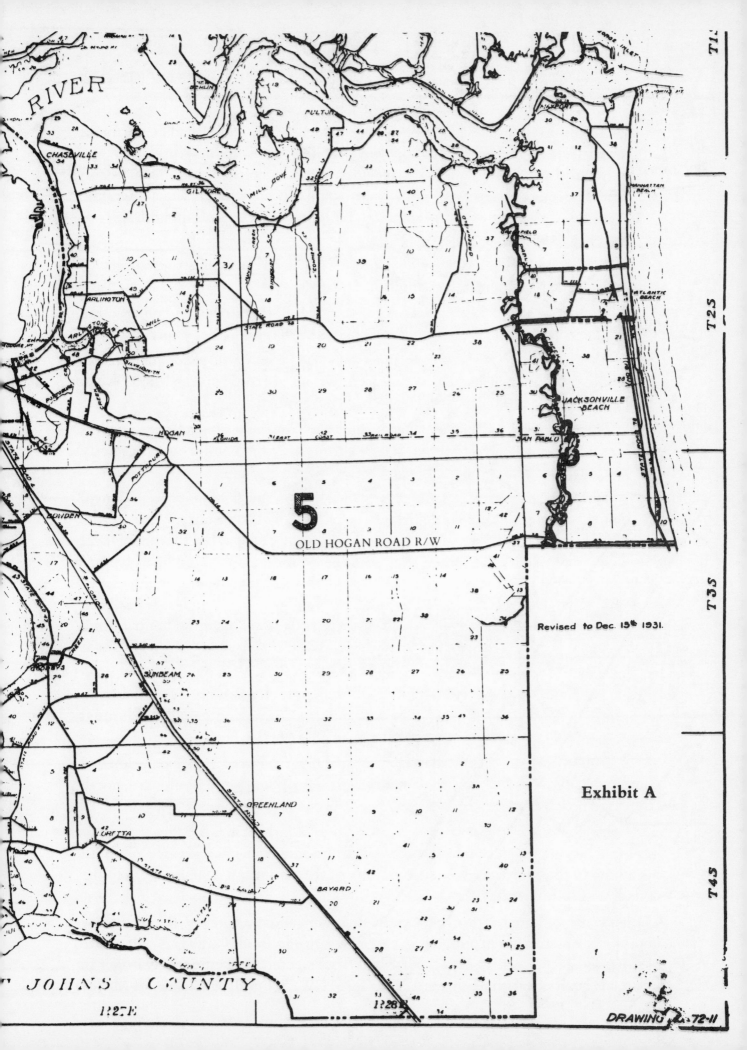

Exhibit A

Exhibit B

© 1969 General Drafting Co., Inc.

Tanzler's University Site Selection Committee stated that "the authority is not interested in building the road unless it can be guaranteed that the site for the university is adjacent to or in close proximity to the road alignment."

Had not the authority in 1968 been in possession of a right of way from U.S. Alternate 1 (Southside Boulevard) easterly to the general area then being considered for the site of a university, the University of North Florida might not be a reality at its present location. Likewise, J. Turner Butler Boulevard would not be a reality today, if the site of the university had been designated to be in another section of Duval County.

Note: The History of J. Turner Butler Boulevard was sent to the Chairman and all members of the JTA by letter of August 25, 1976. A thank you letter dated September 24, 1976 was received from JTA Chairman Wesley C. Paxson on behalf of the Authority. The History was officially accepted into the agency's records without argument.

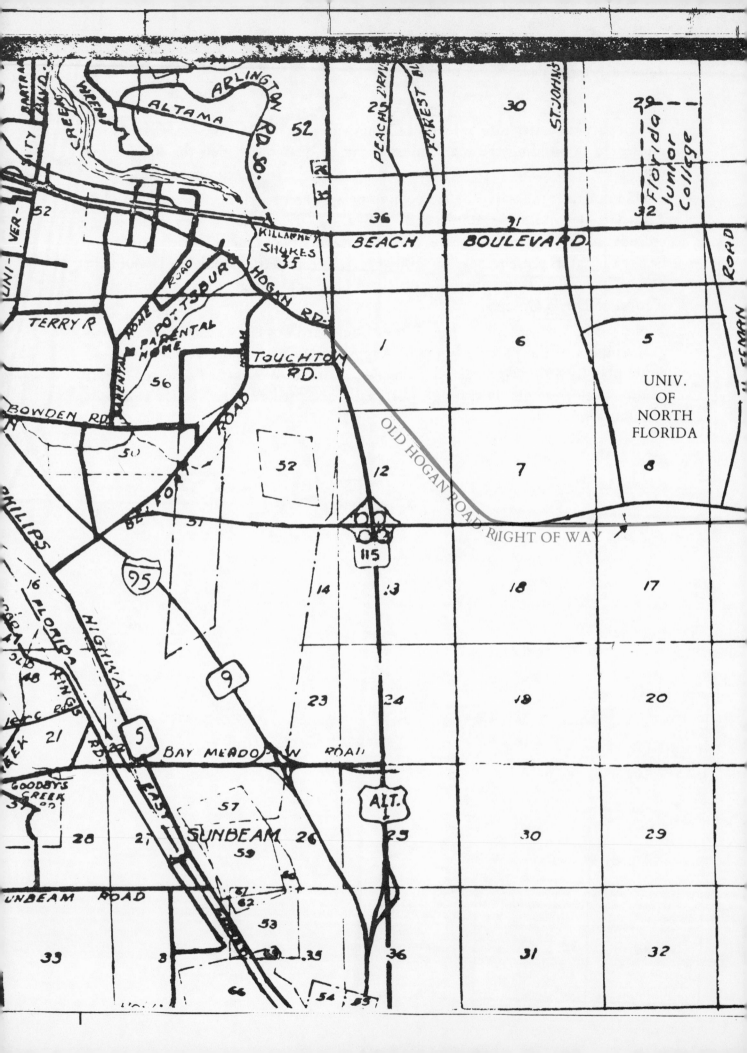

Exhibit C

CHAPTER XXIV
SOME INVOLVED CITIZENS

Beginning with the opening of the Mathews Bridge on April 15, 1953, the Warren Bridge on June 7, 1954, and the Hart Bridge on November 2, 1967, the citizens of Duval County and millions of visitors have enjoyed the privileges of zooming over the network of limited access highways and bridges of the Jacksonville expressway system. To the majority of people the ease of travel, the total absence of traffic lights, is accepted as a way of life. But many cities in Florida and other states have asked on numerous occasions how the expressway system started. What was the origin of the movement? What are the forces that now are keeping the product vigorous and full of life? Will the toll bridges ever be free? Are there any plans for the future? If any, what are these plans?

It was during the Depression years of the 1930's, when money was hard to come by that certain brave citizens dared to advocate the spending of local money for the upgrading of highway facilities.

In 1932 the county commissioners led by Commissioners Joe F. Hammond, Charles W. Herlong and A.T. Brown, advocated the construction of a bridge across the St. Johns River from the vicinity of Beaver Street to Arlington with a direct connection to Atlantic Boulevard. This proposed new route to the Beaches was strongly supported by B.C. Buck, President of the Progressive Freeholders Association, Alston Cockrell, John W. Harrell, Mabry Carlton, John B. Mathews and George M. Powell.

Speaking at one of the mass meetings held on the subject Harrell said, "The new bridge is the most forward step this community has taken since it tried unsuccessfully to obtain voters' approval to the same project two years ago. Let us look ahead, not step backward. If ten years ago you had listened to the men who would lean backwards instead of forward you would have no present St. Johns River Bridge (now Acosta Bridge). Those who oppose the present bridge are now holding up the horror of increased taxation if the new one is built. Most of them are prompted by selfish reasons. Do the forward-looking people of the community believe that Jacksonville has ceased to grow? If they think that, they should move."

Mathews said he was for a new bridge years ago, that it was one of his ideas. He said, "It is my prediction that the new bridge will have enough money to pay off its bonds in 15 years, not 30 as is proposed."

"I'd hang my head in shame if I thought we were 'through' as a community," Mathews said.

Deploring a "campaign of fear" being carried on by opponents of the proposed Arlington Bridge, Powell issued a public statement in which he pointed out that under the law the credit of the county need not be pledged as security for the bridge bonds. He said, "In the first place, the bugaboo about the possible dangers to the taxpayer is just another bit of political hokum, projected, apparently for the purpose of beguiling the overburdened taxpayer into assisting in an attempt to prevent a great public work that will do much, if constructed, not only to provide the city of Jacksonville, that has now crossed the river, with more nearly adequate crossing facilities, but also provide businesses for the material man and the factories behind him, employment for the unemployed, and patronage for the merchant."

The problem, to build or not to build, was decided at the polls by the freeholders on November 15, 1932 by a vote of 5536 against to 4037 for.

For another six years Jacksonville crawled back into its shell and remained there all smug and content with the status quo of federal works until some dormant seeds of progressiveness emerged again in 1938.

This time a number of local civic organizations combined their thinking and formed a Civic Improvement Committee to study bond proposals of the City Commission, County Commission and School Board.

A report of the committee to the free holders of Jacksonville and Duval County was submitted on August 30, 1938 to the respective public bodies. The letter of submittal carried this sentence: "an effort has been made to keep this report free from recommendations and opinions," which in effect made it valueless.

Immediately following the publication of the report, battle lines were drawn and after a month of verbal fireworks, the freeholders said "no" on September 20, to the issuance of bonds for capital improvements in the community.

The County Commission thought the freeholders of the county should be given another opportunity to express their opinion. Accordingly they called for an election on November 8, 1938 on the two projects rejected on September 20th. Their reasoning was the public did not realize the need for an additional artery from Riverside which would have extended May Street by viaduct over the railroad tracks, overcrossing Bay and Forsyth streets to connect to Adams Street.

The St. Johns River bridge crossing would connect downtown Jacksonville to the Arlington area but the main objective was to connect to Atlantic Boulevard for a shorter and faster way to the Beaches. The law in effect at this time stated that in order for a "freeholders" election to be legal, it was necessary that a simple majority of the registered voters cast their ballot. Although 5434 votes were cast in favor of the project to 1360 votes against, the projects failed to carry, as 12,462 votes were needed. A monument to this negative vote is the existing bottleneck at the intersection of the Riverside viaduct and Acosta Bridge.

Human nature is such that it is instantly attracted to the promise of something for nothing. Every gimmick, slogan and promise is garnished, painted and made alluring in order to persuade the masses to fall for these inducements.

For example, the promoters of such ideas had received a setback on November 30, 1931 when the freeholders rejected a proposal to lift the tolls on the St. Johns River Bridge (Acosta Bridge) by a vote of 5032 to 1399.

But persistence is one of the virtues of those who believe in the "Santa Claus" policy, so by a different approach the County Commission was persuaded in 1937 to approve construction of a free bridge across the St. Johns River from the foot of Main Street to the Southside. The catch was that the county would pay half the construction cost, approximately $728,172. The State Road Department, using federal funds, would construct the bridge.

The commission signed a contract on January 6, 1938 with the S.R.D. calling for the construction of the Main Street Bridge. On October 10, 1939 the commissioners signed an agreement to free the Acosta Bridge of tolls as of midnight December 31, 1939.

The new bridge across the St. Johns River was officially dedicated July 18, 1941 by Mrs. Spessard Holland, charming "first lady" of Florida. Governor Holland was assigned the honor of cutting the ribbon.

Throughout the years Duval County has been blessed by having many people contribute to the betterment of the highway network. These persons who should be gratefully remembered are:

Alston W. Cockrell, through whose efforts Duval County was given 50 foot wide strips of land on both sides of the former 100 foot Florida East Coast Railroad right of way (east from Southside Estates to the vicinity of San Pablo Road) which today is a part of Beach Boulevard.

Arthur Penman, for donating to the county practically all of the eighty foot right of way from Atlantic Boulevard to Beach Boulevard for the construction of the road which today bears his name.

George Fish for his unselfish work in helping secure at no cost to the county a lengthy section of the 80 foot right of way of University Boulevard South, between Bartram Road and Atlantic Boulevard.

Edward Lee Stevenson who donated to the county an 80 foot right of way now a part of University Boulevard West, from San Jose Boulevard (State Road 13), easterly through what is now known as the Lakewood section.

The Brown brothers, Saxton and Willie, for making it possible for the county to construct Mt. Pleasant Road most economically. They donated an 80 foot right of way several thousand feet long from the vicinity of "Turkey Knoll," east and southeast to a point near Girvin Road.

D.W. (Sandy) McArthur, for riding horseback over a vast area in the northwest part of Duval County with Fred Stack, of the county engineer's office, obtaining miles of free rights of way for the location of ditches and canals that were so essential to the drainage of many of the county's roads.

The Model Land Company of St. Augustine, Florida, through their Mr. Fox, who deeded, at no cost to the county, the former 100 foot width right of way of the Jacksonville, Mayport and Pablo Railway from Ft. Caroline Road easterly to Seminole Beach Road. At this time McCormick Road, a part of Girvin Road and Wonderwood Drive utilize a great portion of the old railroad roadbed.

Francis Johnson, well known for his great work among children, for his ready response and willingness in giving rights of way when asked for roads, and land for playgrounds.

William R. Cesery for the part he played in obtaining, at no cost to the county, a 100 foot right of way approximately a mile long, for drainage purposes, extending easterly from the Lake Lucina area to Red Bay Branch.

Seven Skinner brothers, B.J., Ben, R.G., A.C., Sr., E.E., W.D., and J.F., who gave to the county all of the rights of way for the original Bowden Road alignment from Hogan Road southerly and westerly to existing U.S. 1.

Richard G. Skinner and A. Chester Skinner, Sr. for donating a two hundred foot right of way for Southside Boulevard from Beach Boulevard South to U.S. 1.

A. Chester Skinner, Jr., Brightman Skinner and their sister, Mary Virginia Jones, for giving to the Jacksonville Expressway Authority a two hundred and fifty foot strip of land for the construction of the first section of J. Turner Butler Boulevard from the site of the University of North Florida westerly for approximately two miles.

THE CITY PLANNING AND ADVISORY BOARD

The City Planning and Advisory Board had been acutely aware of the many shortcomings of the city in all of its public works departments, particularly the need to upgrade existing city streets and project new arterials. Accordingly a Streets and Highways Committee was appointed in the spring of 1945 by Board President S. Ralph Fetner to investigate the city's proposed five-year postwar highway program.

The committee, composed of Arthur N. Sollee as chairman, Ralph Spaulding, A.E. Brown and W.B. Simmons submitted their findings in a report dated June 26, 1945.

While agreeing that the program of reconstruction and construction of highways and bridges for Jacksonville, as submitted by City Engineer, W.E. Sheddan, to the City Commission was sound, the committee felt that special attention should be given to studies and surveys of possible north and south through-traffic routes connecting the southern part of the city to the northern part.

This report speaks for itself and is quoted as submitted.

Studies and surveys should be made of possible north and south through traffic routes connecting the southern part of the city with the northern part. At present the north and south interchange routes are as follows:

Edgewood Avenue; part of Myrtle Avenue; a small section of Davis Street; Pearl Street; Main Street, Florida Avenue and Phoenix Avenue; and Talleyrand Avenue.

These streets are inadequate to take care of the north and south flow of heavy commercial traffic, so the committee recommends that the following streets be made through north and south traffic routes:

(a) Buckman Street, between 31st Street and 8th Street.

(b) Haines Street, between 8th Street and Adams Street.

(c) Fairfax Street, between 21st Street and Acorn Street.

(d) Acorn Street, between Fairfax Street and Beaver Street (or Lake City Road).

(e) McMillan Street, from 21st Street southerly to and across Kings Road, to a point about 5th Street; thence southwesterly by means of a viaduct across the Atlantic Coast Line Railroad and Georgia-Southern and Florida Railroad tracks to Orchard Street; thence southwesterly along Orchard Street to Hartridge Street; thence southerly along Line Street to Beaver Street (or Lake City Road), to meet the northerly projection of King Street.

(f)   Division Street starting at its intersection with 21st Street; thence southerly along Division Street across Kings Road to approximately 10th Street; thence south-westerly by an overpass across the Atlantic Coast Line Railroad yards and the Georgia-Southern and Florida Railroad to a point at the approximate intersection of McDuff Avenue and Fifth Street; thence south on McDuff Avenue to Roosevelt Boulevard.

(g)   Huron Street, starting at its intersection with Beaver Street; thence southerly on Huron Street by way of a viaduct across the Seaboard Line Railway yards to the intersection of Warrington Avenue and Nelson Street; thence southerly on Nelson Street to Post Street.

The proposed viaducts across the A.C.L. yards and Georgia-Southern and Florida Railroad will do much to eliminate the terribly congested Myrtle Avenue route. A careful study of the map on which all of the proposed routes are located clearly indicates just what will take place by their construction, for at present there are no through north and south traffic routes between Edgewood Avenue and Myrtle Avenue.

The westerly and easterly streets and roads are fairly well developed but it is felt that the addition of another entrance from the west into Jacksonville would be of untold value to the commercial interests as well as relieve the serious traffic congestion on Post Street.

It has been proposed by the State Road Department that the north fork of State Road No. 204 (now Normandy Boulevard) should be extended from Lenox Avenue, at its intersection with Dorset Street in a northeasterly direction along a curve meeting a westerly extension of Fitzgerald Street; thence easterly along Fitzgerald Street and McCoy's Creek Boulevard to Myrtle Avenue; thence north on Myrtle Avenue to Bay Street. The existing Myrtle Avenue underpass to be widened and given more headroom.

This route is a necessity and is recommended as it would be the southerly east and west interchange for commercial traffic in Jacksonville and would be comparable to the proposed State Road Department east and west traffic interchange on 21st Street from State Road No. 4 to Talleyrand Avenue. Beaver Street (or Lake City Road) is the middle east and west interchange.

Beaver Street should be opened and extended easterly from Washington Street, with a viaduct across Hogan Creek to meet a westerly projection of Albert Street, thence on Albert Street to Talleyrand Avenue. This new east and west traffic artery would tap the business and commercial area in East Jacksonville and also serve as a potential outlet for the proposed bridge across the St. Johns River to Arlington.

The committee has also noted that there is a very dangerous condition existing at the intersection of Adams Street and Lee Street. It is recommended that the southeast corner of this intersection be acquired by the city of Jacksonville in order to relieve this situation. Lee Street should be widened from Adams Street northerly to State Street and extended northerly from State Street to an intersection with Davis Street.

Several years ago extensive work was done on Beaver Street, between Lee and Eaverson streets. Unfortunately the curves were not eliminated at that time, so it is suggested that steps be taken to relieve a condition which is fast becoming intolerable.

Prior to the war, traffic counts made by the State Road Department showed that the traffic on Main Street, across the Trout River Bridge, was predominantly higher than at a point on Main Street at its intersection with Dunn Avenue. World War II has added a vast impetus to air travel and therefore, the expected traffic between Jacksonville Municipal Airport No. 1 and the city proper will be increased by leaps and bounds and the existing bridge over Trout River will be most inadequate. Travel destined for Heckscher Drive, which is now toll free will further aggravate the situation. Therefore, the committee recommends that steps be taken by the city to work with the State Road Department toward the construction of an additional and adequate bridge across Trout River at Pearl Street.

The committee further recommends that the city cooperate with the county as far as possible in the construction of a bridge across Moncrief Creek at the foot of Tallulah Avenue. This bridge would provide the last missing link in an around-the-city route by way of Edgewood Avenue.

In the post-war improvement program the city has set up under "bridges and viaducts" the sum of $750,000 for a viaduct over the railroad yards on a southerly prolongation of Davis Street. The purpose of this viaduct would be to divert some of the Riverside traffic from the Broad Street and Lee Street viaducts and Myrtle Avenue underpass. The committee feels that while this particular project appears to have much merit, that it is of the opinion that it could be advantageously eliminated, provided viaducts or overpasses were constructed as recommended by the committee at the northerly extremities of King Street and McDuff Avenue over the A.C.L.R.R. and the Georgia-Southern and Florida Railway track. As previously pointed out these last named overpasses would divert much of the commercial traffic now using the Broad Street and Lee Street viaducts and the Myrtle Avenue underpass.

Another recommendation of the city engineer's office to the City Commission is an expenditure of approximately $750,000 for the acquisition of properties and construction of a new street approximately two blocks east and two blocks west of Main Street on the waterfront on the north side of the St. Johns River. The purpose is to obtain this roadway or street passing underneath the Main Street Bridge so that traffic conditions at the existing intersection of Bay and Main streets will be relieved. The lands created would extend from the existing bulkheads southerly to the pierhead line as established by the U.S. Engineer Department and besides being used for the much desired underpass, could be used for many other public purposes. Such a proposal meets with the approval of this committee, for, by creating such new lands the existing unsightly appearance of the waterfront on both sides of the Main Street Bridge would be eliminated and Jacksonville would then be in a position to boast of a much sought for and dreamed of beautiful waterfront.

One of the most neglected areas and undeveloped portions as far as interchange of traffic is concerned is the south side of the river. With the imminent construction of the Hogan Road, steps should be taken to eliminate as much travel as possible that originates west of the Florida East Coast Railway from having to come all the way into the business section in order to go to the Beaches. It is proposed that surveys and studies should be made to open up a route from River Oaks Road easterly along Garland and Wishart Streets; thence along San Diego Road, Stillman Street and Carmichael Avenue and thence to the Hogan Road. Studies also should be made to extend Ashland Street easterly from the Old St. Augustine Road by means of an underpass under the Florida East Coast Railway and Philips Highway, thence easterly to the Hogan Road. This last named proposed route, although now in the county, will not in the too distant future be needed to relieve the already overtaxed intersection at Atlantic Boulevard, and Kings Avenue.

In making the above recommendations for investigations and possible construction the committee feels that this work should be done as soon as possible, for the recent census has demonstrated that the city and county are growing with amazing rapidity. Students of traffic have long known that proper steps should be taken to develop through traffic routes within the city, but due to lack of finances and proper publicity, nothing has ever been done.

It should be noted that this report covers certain recommendations that come within the jurisdiction of the county commissioners but it is felt that due to the close tie-up of traffic problems within the city and county that there should be created some workable setup whereby the traffic problems of the city and county could be solved simultaneously. The recent census has shown the tremendous increase in suburban population over that within the city. This means that the county's and the city's traffic problems are one and the same and should be approached with the one purpose in mind of giving better and more adequate interchange facilities between business and commercial districts, residential areas and the recreational facilities at the Beaches. Close cooperation between a city-county traffic committee would definitely work to the benefit of the traveling public.

The committee has strived to do a real service for the people of the city and county; with this in view has made the various studies with its recommendations. It is hoped that the City Planning Advisory Board does not feel that its Road and Bridge Committee has overstepped its bounds, for this work has been done in the best of faith.

The City Commission did not bother with or attempt to follow any of the recommendations enumerated in the report so the efforts of the committee turned out to be a waste of time.

CHAPTER XXVI
BRIDGES THAT BIND

The modern bridge is a striking symbol of man's creativeness and ingenuity in overcoming the obstacle courses nature has provided to hinder and slow him in his never ending search of new fields to conquer. Although having a fear of the never ending flow of the streams and rivers, nevertheless he always has had an irresistible urge and longing to investigate and explore on the other side that which he could not see with his limited vision.

Old folk tales and legends reveal that the bridging of a stream by man was thought to be an affront to the river gods, and to pacify and appease their wrath and anger, it was the custom to offer human sacrifice to the sullen stream.

Even today, among certain steel workers who walk so casually high above the rivers, bays and estuaries, there are omens that portray good and evil and are a part of their workday life.

The five highway bridges that span the St. Johns River are outstanding examples of the skill that has been developed by engineers in accommodating the various modes of transportation.

Depending upon the point of view these bridges may be described in various ways.

An engineer would tell you the Acosta and Alsop bridges were vertical lift spans, the Warren Bridge a double leaf bascule, the Mathews a three span cantilever truss, and the new Hart Bridge a three span cantilever truss with a suspended roadway center span.

The everyday commuter would extoll on the bridges as being the means for a swift and hurried journey to and from work. And a land developer would present reams of statistics to prove that by using a certain bridge his houses would be ideally situated to serve the needs of his prospective client.

A proud citizen would tell the world that the construction of each new bridge denotes an ever growing community, a story of achievement and the steel and concrete reflect the strength and sturdiness of its citizenry. Yes, in truthfulness he can state that the five river bridges are the sinews that have bridged the gap and are cohesive and inseparable chains that now bind together the "Bold New City of the South."

But to many, bridges are more than mere concrete and steel— they are the epitome of beauty and splendor. They are silent citadels rising in majesty to greet the sky and reflect their glory as moving shadows on the shifting water.

The spirit of the "Bold New City" has been captured for posterity in color photographs that show the graceful and serene line of the gaunt and silent Hart Bridge being silhouetted by a Florida sun sliding gracefully to bed amidst the ever changing yellowish tinted clouds skipping among the glow of pinks and browns and chartreuse.

And from a bridge-eye's view the panoramic scene seems to say: Stop, "Bold New City" on the day of your birth. Open your eyes so that you may see that which physically binds together the land masses that now constitute your entity.

Note: *Bridges That Bind,* by the author appeared in the *Florida Times Union* issue of October 1, 1968.

"OFFICIAL" INFORMATION
ST. JOHNS RIVER BRIDGE

Board of County Commissioners - January 1935

J. G. CARY	Dist. 1	ELLIOT W. BUTTS	Clerk
RAY GREENE	Dist. 2	R. A. MILLS (5-0812)	Secretary
J. F. HAMMOND	Dist. 3		
C. H. SIMPSON	Dist. 4	T. O. KESLER	
D. C. BROWN	Dist. 5	Bridge Supt.	
		Phone 5-1768	

POLICE DEPARTMENT PHONE   3-1056
FIRE DEPARTMENT PHONE   5-0172

COUNTY DEPARTMENTS

Agricultural Dept.	5-7092
Armory, Market St.	5-8777
Auto Tag Office	5-5113
Supt. St. Johns Bridge	5-1768
Chairman Co. Com.	5-0312
Circuit Court Chambers	5-1299
Civil Court Chambers	5-0643
Clerk Circuit Court	5-0812
Clerk Civil Court	5-0727
Clerk Criminal Court	3-0597
Law Dept.	5-1169
Accounting Dept.	5-6734
Clerk's Office	5-6023
County Commissioners	5-0812
Delinquent Tax Dept.	5-0378
County Judges	5-2246
Criminal Court Room	5-4274
Engineer's Office	5-3279
Jail, 635 Liberty St.	5-0111
Juvenile Court	5-3567
Parental Home	3-1383J
Plumbing Inspector	5-1681
County Prison Farm Supt.	7-4411
Supt.'s Residence	7-2163
Prosecuting Atty.	5-2379
Purchasing Agent	5-4777
Road Patrol	5-1681
Sheriff's Office, Day	5-0393
Sheriff's Office, Night	5-0111
Supervisor Registration	5-2383
Tax Assessor	5-8771
Tax Collector	5-1772
Duval County Hospital	3-0906
County Welfare Board	3-0505

RECAPITULATION

318	$318,000	$310,709.86
344	$344,000	$357,392.51
662	$662,000	$668,102.37
Less Interest Collected		$ 6,425.00
Net Cost of Bonds		$661,677.37

By the purchase of these Bonds before maturity, the Tax Payers of Duval County have been saved approximately One Million Dollars.

The original Bond Issue to construct this Bridge was for Twelve Hundred Thousand Dollars, and all of these Bonds have been bought and paid for, except Ninety Thousand Dollars worth, which do not reach maturity until 1948, and these outstanding Bonds bear an interest rate of 5%, and the holders of these Bonds will not surrender them to the County, until they reach maturity.

FINANCIAL CONDITION

Duval County today is in the best financial condition of any County almost in the entire United States and by the continued use of the revenue off of this Bridge, which by the way does not work any great hardship on any individual or firm. The Board of County Commissioners can and will contniue to use these funds for the benefit of the people of this County to the end that Taxes and Bonded indebtedness can be greatly decreased. Of this $124,000 that the bridge earned last year approximately 65% was paid by the tourist. So why should we people of Duval County surrender this, our greatest asset, while the Metropolitan City of New York retains her toll bridges and enjoys the profits.

FREE BRIDGE

In the event this Bridge was made free of Tolls, who would pay this 5% interest on the Ninety Thousand Dollars worth of Bonds that do not mature until 1948? Who would pay for the maintenance and upkeep on this bridge which actually costs Ten Thousand Dollars a year to maintain? Who would pay for any accident or mishap that could at any time for some unforseen reason happen to this structure, which would necessitate the expenditure of a goodly sum of money for repair? Who would pay the salaries of the ten or twelve men that the Government would require to be kept on this bridge, even though it were free to keep the mechanism of this structure in first class condition and to operate the draw bridge according to Government requirements?

Is it not better to let everyone who uses this structure and enjoys the privilege of its use every hour of the day and night to share in this responsibility of paying a small toll, which by the way in proportion to its actual cost and upkeep is the most economical toll bridge in the entire United States, rather than to place this entire burden on the shoulders of the already heavy laden few? As the situation now stands, the people of Duval County are the recipients from the revenues of this bridge to the extent of approximately One Hundred and Fifty Thousand Dollars net profit per year, which actually means the equivalent of three mills taxation saved for the people.

ROAD MILEAGE

JACKSONVILLE TO TAMPA

Jacksonville	0.0
Baldwin	19.2
Lawtey	38.6
Starke	46.0
Hampton	52.5
Waldo	54.8
Fairbanks	65.3
Gainesville	72.0
Micanopy	89.5
McIntosh	95.2
Reddick	100.7
Ocala	111.0
Dunnellon	135.0
Brooksville	177.0
Tampa	222.0

Jacksonville to Jacksonville Beach and St. Augustine

So. Jacksonville	1.0
St. Nicholas	2.3
Jacksonville Bh	21.0
St. Augustine	40.0

JACKSONVILLE TO MIAMI

So. Jacksonville	1.0
Bayard	17.0
St. Augustine	39.0
Cross Bridge	
Anastasia Isl.	41.0
Mantanzas Inlet Bridge	56.0
Flagler Beach	72.0
Ormond Beach	83.5
Daytona Beach	88.0
Cross Bridge Daytona Main Station	91.2
Port Orange	96.6
New Smyrna	106.4
Oak Hill	118.5
Titusville	139.9
Cocoa	158.8
Rockledge	160.5
Eau Gallie	176.0
Melbourne	180.5
Grant	192.4
Sebastian	201.5
Vero	214.7
Fort Pierce	226.0
Stuart	249.0
Hobe Sound	262.0
Jupiter	268.7
Riviera	282.5
W. Palm Bch.	287.2
Palm Beach	288.5
Delray	307.0
Ft. Lauderdale	331.8
Lemon City	353.5
Miami	356.0

ANNUAL TOLL TAGS

Must be permanently fastened on front Bracket of Machine.

All pleasure cars exclusive of buses annually	$ 6.00
Light two-wheel trailers, attached to cars*	6.00
Trucks up to One Ton	7.50
Trucks to 2 tons	15.00
Trucks all over 2 tons	25.00

From July 1st for remainder of year tags are sold at one half of above rates.

For further information Telephone Bridge Superintendent, 5-1768.

TOLL RATES—JACKSONVILLE-ST. JOHNS RIVER BRIDGE

CLASSIFICATION	Single Trip	Round Trip	Commutation or Ticket Books		
			Trips	Cost	Cost Per Trip
Automobiles—to 3049 pounds, with driver	.20	.35	20	2.00	.10
Automobiles—3049 pounds and under, with driver	.15	.25	16	1.25	.08
Vehicle passengers	.03	.05	50	.75	.01½
Foot Passengers (or person on bicycle)	$ .01	$.......	50	$ .50	$ .01
Motorcycles and drivers (single or side car)	.10	.15	15	1.00	.06⅔
Horse and rider	.10	.15	15	1.00	.06⅔
Trucks—1 ton and under, with driver	.15	.25	16	1.25	.08
Trucks over 1 ton and under 2 tons, with driver	.20	.35	20	2.00	.10
Trucks of 2 tons and not over 3 tons, with driver	.20	.35	.20	2.75	.13¾
Trucks of more than 3 tons and not over 5 tons, with driver	.25	.40	20	3.50	.17½
Trucks of more than 5 tons, with driver	.50	.90	....	....	....
Sightseeing cars or buses, with driver and passengers	.50	.80	50	15.00	.30
Horse and vehicle, with driver	.15	.25	....	....	....
Driven live stock, per head	.05	....	....	....	....
Double team and driver	.20	.35	....	....	....
Lumber wagon, 30 feet or more over all, with driver	.35	.60	....	....	....
Trailers (2 wheel) attached to pleasure cars	.15	.25	16	1.25	.08

COMPARATIVE TOLLS AND HOW THEY APPLY TO ALL USERS OF THE BRIDGE

For the sum of $6.00 per year, any Automobile owner can purchase at the Court House at room 101 which is the Clerks office a Bridge Tag, after attaching this Tag to the front bracket of his or her car, they have the privilege of using this Bridge day and night as many times as they care to, hauling as many passengers as they can get into the Car for this sum. This Tag is good for Twelve months of the year. On July the first which is the half year period, this same Tag can be bought for $3.00 which is good for the remaining six months of the year with the same privileges.

Contrast

A foot passenger who is perhaps unable to own an Automobile and cannot afford a Car pays in Toll for the privilege of walking across this Bridge 1c each way or Two Cents a day, and pays in Toll in the year's time $7.30, and can only walk over for that a limited number of times, whereas an Automobile owner only pays $6.00 in the year's time hauling as many passengers as he cares to, and using the Bridge at his own discretion, and it actually only costs the Auto Owner 11½c per week for this privilege. While the man on foot pays 14c per week, and can only make 7 round trips for that sum.

SENATE BILL NO. 174

This Bill was passed by the Legislature in the 1933 session and is known as Senate Bill 174. The purpose of this Bill was to delegate and empower, the Board of County Commissioners, and the Board of Bond Trustees of the St. Johns River Bridge Fund, to use the funds on hand and all accrueing revenue of the Bridge to purchase and retire any Bonded indebtedness of Duval County, except a sinking fund that must be kept on hand of $50,000 this $50,000 to be used only in emergency in the event of something happening to the bridge.

Since the enactment of this bill, the County Commissioners and the Board of Bond Trustees have bought out of the bridge revenues the following bonds:

Issue of		No.	Cost plus
1909	Good Roads	56	$ 54,610.14
1920	Refunding	234	249,730.00
1923	Roads	2	1,940.00
1925	Roads	52	51,076.81
	Total	344	$357,392.51

Serial Bridge Bonds Issue of 1923

No. of Bonds	Par Val.	Accd. Int. Cost Plus
101	$101,000	$ 98,408.33

Serial Road Bonds Issue of 1923

217	$217,000	$212,301.53
318	$318,000	$310,709.86

JACKSONVILLE ST. JOHNS RIVER BRIDGE

Work started on this Bridge November 15, 1919, and the bridge was completed and opened to the public July the 1st, 1921.

Length of the bridge over the water is 2370 feet, and including both approaches is 3740 over all.

Lift Span Towers are 165 feet above their supporting piers, or 222 feet above the water. Floor of the Lift Span is 65 feet above the water in the main channel, leaving a vertical clearance under bridge when closed of 57 feet.

Lift span can be raised so as to give a clearance under bridge of 165 feet.

The bridge cost, inclusive of all services in connection with the construction, $1,-187,862.94.

All indebtedness against this bridge has been paid, except Ninety Thousand Dollars worth of bonds that do not mature until 1948, these bonds bear an interest rate of 5%.

This bridge earned for the people of Duval County during the year 1934 over and above all operating and maintenance expenses, $124,351.67.

For further information about how revenue is expended see other page about Senate Bill No. 174 Act of 1933 Legislature.

THE 1990 PLAN

The first page of Section B of the Wednesday, July 30, 1969 edition of *The Florida Times-Union* greeted the reader with these headlines across the top of the page: "Sweeping Expressway Study Authorized." The article by Otis Perkins stated the Expressway Authority at its Tuesday meeting authorized preliminary engineering studies for a construction program projected to serve local needs until 1990. He added that in its resolution calling for the study, the authority had taken similar action March 28, 1967.

The authority immediately authorized that such preliminary engineering studies be undertaken by the firms of Sverdrup and Parcel and Reynolds, Smith and Hills.

A few months later in a special session held by the authority on October 3, 1969 it voted unanimously to accept the proposals of the two firms for studies involving many miles of expressway routes based upon their preliminary findings.

Prior to the above actions by the authority the State Road Department announced in *The Florida Times-Union* of May 9, 1968, that comprehensive studies of the Jacksonville Metropolitan Area would begin about May 16, 1968 in an effort to determine how and why its more than half a million residents travel within the area and to learn what they expect in community services. These studies when completed and analyzed were to become the foundation upon which the 1990 plan was based.

An excellent article in the March 11, 1970 edition of the *Times-Union* by Mike Tolbert was the first public coverage of proposed expansion plans by Sverdrup and Parcel and Associates, Inc. which had been sent to the Duval Area Planning Board and other public officials for their reaction. The plan had not been approved by the authority as it was only in the discussion stage. Marvin Hill, executive director for the Planning Board was quoted as saying he was a little dubious of the JEA study as it didn't conform to their 1990 plan. When pressed for more specific information I stressed that the proposed new traffic corridor was strictly a preliminary study which would have to go for consideration before: the Planning Board; various Jacksonville civic groups; the Highway Committee of the Chamber of Commerce; and a firm of consultants studying downtown Jacksonville development.

The Jacksonville Area Planning Board's first scheduled public meeting to discuss planning was held at Wolfson High School on April 1, 1970. It was chaired by Marvin Hill, executive director of the board. After much discussion it appeared that most of those present feared the proposed expressway from downtown Jacksonville to Old St. Augustine Road near Interstate 295 would split up residential areas and be near schools. A vote was taken on the issue and nearly all of those present voted their disapproval.

Mayor Hans Tanzler at his press conference held April 9, 1970 announced that he had written Planning Board Chairman William K. Jackson concerning expansion of the expressway system. Tanzler was quoted as saying: "While these expressway routes are still in the discussion stage, I think it most important that the Jacksonville-Duval Area Planning Board be given the opportunity to critique the proposed routes." Evidently the mayor had forgotten the contents of the following letter dated July 31, 1969:

The Honorable Hans G. Tanzler, Jr.
Mayor of Jacksonville
City Hall
Jacksonville, Florida 32202

Dear Mr. Tanzler:

At the regular meeting of the Jacksonville Expressway Authority held on Tuesday, July 29, 1969, the attached resolution was proposed by Mr. Richard J. Lewinson and unanimously adopted by the authority.

You can be assured that, as stated in the resolution, all engineering studies will include the thinking and help of all public bodies and citizens of the city and Duval County.

Very truly yours,

Arthur N. Sollee
Executive Director

ANS:p
Enclosure

Frank Young, staff writer for the *Times-Union* on May 3, 1970, in a well written synopsis of conflicts looming over the expressway future had this to report:

Arthur Sollee, JEA executive director as to the opposition generated by the suggested route through the Arlington area, said alternates suggested were not feasible. He pointed out that apartments were springing up everywhere near Regency Square, so how are these people going to get downtown? If the authority doesn't provide a second expressway link into the core city, current rush hour traffic jams to the Mathews Bridge will be minor in comparison.

The executive director further stated, should such a proposed new link not be provided, a few years from now people will be demanding to know "why somebody didn't do something about this before."

Young, in his interview with Marvin Hill, executive director of the Planning Board quoted Hill as saying "there is a good bit of difference" in suggestions for major thoroughfare corridors. "The new (JEA) corridors don't show up in our plans." Hill also stated the Expressway Authority's placing an entirely new major expressway corridor from its 8th Street leg, south across the river around the Acosta Bridge continuing southward, crossing Sunbeam Road in Mandarin and tying in with Old St. Augustine road, is unnecessary.

Hill's reason for stating the new corridor to the Mandarin area was unnecessary, was that traffic now flows in parallel thoroughfares over Interstate 95, four-laned Philips Highway, four-laned State Road 13. In addition, he said Old St. Augustine Road currently is being widened.

Hill told Young the Planning Board's consultants, Barbour Cooper & Associates and Allen M. Voorhees & Associates, were aiding in the critique requested by Mayor Tanzler.

The *Jacksonville Journal* on July 3, 1970 headlined a story by Paul McGinty; "Expressway Plans Meet Strong Opposition." McGinty quoted Planning Board Director Marvin Hill as saying he was worried about Arlington's fate with an expressway through its center. "If it goes right through this community, it would violate the concept of the residential community," he said.

The same day, July 3, 1970, Frank Young, *Florida Times-Union* staff writer, reported in some detail on a meeting held on Thursday in City Hall which had been called by Mayor Hans Tanzler for a "workshop" session to better coordinate expressway projects and the plans of other agencies. Those attending the session were Roger L. Main, chairman, JEA, James Gast, representing Sverdrup & Parcel, the authority's consulting engineers, representatives of the State Department of Transportation, City Department of Housing and Urban Development, Jacksonville Area Planning Board and other agencies.

At the beginning Chairman Main advised the group that the authority "has no programs. There has been no action. We are merely making studies. These studies may never bear fruit. They may never be built."

In response to a question, Main said that the authority as a state agency, is responsive to the people. "We are not going to do anything the people do not want."

Tanzler suggested the Area Planning Board be the coordination agency for all programs, including Expressway Authority proposals.

Sverdrup & Parcel's representative James Gast told the gathering the chosen expressway corridors would eliminate bottlenecks at the Riverside interchange, Fuller Warren Bridge and Mathews Bridge.

For those who value important events in the history of the Bold New City of the South, it was most fortunate that *The Florida Times-Union* delegated Frank Young to cover a briefing October 15, 1970 by Mayor Hans Tanzler and Marvin Hill, executive director of the Jacksonville Area Planning Board on a report and recommendations of a study, undertaken at the mayor's request several months previously by the Planning Board, the city's Department of Housing and Urban Development and other agencies.

This news item by Young is of such significance that it is reproduced here in its entirety.

★ ★ ★ ★ ★ ★   THE FLORIDA TIMES-UNION, JACKSONVILLE, FRIDAY, OCTOBER 16, 1970   B-9

City Asks Expressway Delay Until Evaluation of Study

By FRANK YOUNG
Staff Writer

The city administration is asking the Jacksonville Expressway Authority (JEA) to d e l a y expressway planning until evaluation is completed of the Jacksonville Urban Area Transportation S t u d y (JUATS).

Mayor Hans Tanzler said Thursday delay will allow a greater degree of coordination and comprehensive planning.

Tanzler and Marvin Hill, executive director of the Jacksonville Area Planning Board, briefed newsmen on a report and recommendations of a study undertaken at the mayor's r e q u e s t several months ago by the Planning Board, the city's Department of Housing and Urban Development and other agencies.

HILL CALLED IT the first "extensive study of expressway authority proposals." Tanzler said the recommendations would allow total planning with a greater amount of information available. Other information is outdated, he said.

Planning Board Chairman William K. Jackson, in a cover letter with the report, said a great deal of information has been compiled by the Planning Board and the Florida Department of Transportation (DOT), information now being evaluated by the transportation consultant firm of Harland Bartholomew and Associates, under contract with the state. That study is referred to as JUATS.

JACKSON SAID when completed, JUATS will be recognized as the official transportation plan for the Jacksonville area by DOT and the U.S. Bureau of Public Roads.

"This will be the first time such a comprehensive transportation plan has been developed for this area; and future federal funding for transportation will be based on this study."

Recognizing "the outstanding accomplishments" of the expressway authority to date, Jackson said, "Our future road plan, then, for a large part, will be built around the existing expressway system.

"While roads, especially expressways, directly affect all future development, it is our concern all future roads be a part of the comprehensive planning program."

JACKSON SAID the planning board has been "assured that, in the very near future, the Florida Department of Transportation will be in a position to present some preliminary findings that should assist the JEA in evaluating their proposed routes.

"Our most important recommendation is, therefore, that expressway planning be delayed until these findings are available," he said.

Other general observations by Jackson included:

● That the technical and policy coordinating committees (formal committees created for JUATS) should review the expressway proposals as a part of the study and their recommendations be included.

● That the location of circumferential routes to distribute traffic to various parts of the city rather than to converge all roads upon the downtown area be a part of the total study.

● That mass transportation should be considered in the location of expressways, especially as the city approaches the need for a sophisticated rapid transit system.

● Study must be given to feeder streets to the expressways, and improvements to the feeders should be programed with the consideration of the expressways.

Specific recommendations were made for each route proposal, which the mayor earlier emphasized are "proposed tentative routes."

AMONG T H O S E recommendations is that a new expressway bridge be constructed in the vicinity of the 20th Street leg of the system rather than Eighth Street, with the route on the easterly bank of the St. Johns River running through the Ft. Caroline area instead of the center of Arlington as proposed by the JEA.

The report also said that from "available information" a new route through the San Jose-Mandarin area is not needed. Both that route and the Arlington routes had resulted in strong protests from citizens living in those areas.

The report indicated further study also is needed on other proposed routes.

After receiving the October 15, 1970 letter from Mayor Hans Tanzler, Expressway Authority Chairman Roger Main sent the following:

MEMORANDUM

FROM: Roger L. Main, Chairman
Jacksonville Expressway Authority

TO: Members Jacksonville Expressway Authority

DATE: November 9, 1970

By this time you undoubtedly have read the October 15, 1970 letter to me from the Honorable Mayor Tanzler, Jr., with the accompanying comments and recommendations by the Jacksonville Area Planning Board.

As the authority must cooperate with the city, it is my suggestion that at the next meeting of the authority to be held on Thursday at 2:30 P.M. this November 12, consideration be given that all preliminary expressway expansion studies now being made by the consulting engineering firms of Sverdrup & Parcel and Associates, Inc., and Reynolds, Smith and Hills be suspended until such time as the Florida Department of Transportation transportation proposals for Jacksonville are available.

It is suggested that the authority request the mayor ask the Jacksonville Area Planning Board to give to the authority definite and precise recommendations as to alignments of limited access facilities. These recommendations can then be submitted to the authority's traffic engineers and a determination made if the projects can be financed.

Roger L. Main
Chairman

RLM:p

At the November 12, 1970 authority meeting the following was read into the minutes:

MEMORANDUM

FROM: The Jacksonville Expressway Authority

DATE: November 12, 1970

It has become increasingly evident in recent months to all interested public bodies that additional highways and bridges must be constructed in Jacksonville to avoid the massive traffic congestion which inevitably strangles developing urban communities. Only those communities willing to plan ahead and willing to commence the necessary construction in timely fashion have been able to avoid this destructive congestion. In the past, Jacksonville has been among the leaders in the country in this regard, primarily because of the creation by the Florida Legislature of the autonomous Jacksonville Expressway Authority, which has been given the authority to engineer, construct and pay for the highways and bridges necessary for a developing Jacksonville. It goes without saying that this progress could never have been accomplished without the thorough-going cooperation of the local govenmental agencies, such as the former county government, and the city of Jacksonville, together with the elected political leaders of the community.

Even more important, the Jacksonville expressway system required and has always had almost unanimous public support. This support from the public was absolutely necessary and very gratifying, particularly in view of the fact that the construction of highways has such a profound effect upon a great number of people. Some people will always be dislodged and inconvenienced, although under our eminent domain laws, full monetary compensation to the people is provided. Nevertheless, the local people have always seemed to appreciate the first-class expressway system existing in Jacksonville and the need for future planning and additional construction to stay ahead of the mounting traffic requirements, even though it always has been recognized that there will be some individual disruption of homes and neighborhoods.

The Expressway Authority has as its primary responsibility the construction and preservation of a first-class roadway system which will continue to serve the needs of this community. Growth is necessary so that the existing system will not become strangled with traffic and thus inconvenience the traveling public. The system, therefore, must be designed to meet the maximum traffic demands of the city to offer the maximum convenience to Jacksonville motorists and to generate sufficient revenue to pay the substantial cost of any new additions to the expressway system. Under our statutory authority and under the provisions of our existing trust indentures, no new construction can be commenced without the approval of nationally recognized traffic engineers who will attest that the new facilities will have sufficient traffic volume so that the combined toll facilities will continue to pay the cost of the expanded expressway system.

Finally, the Expressway Authority reasonably must coordinate its actions with all other public agencies and bodies which would be affected by new highway construction. For example, it has already been noted that the present expressway system was achieved only through the joint efforts and cooperation of the authority and the local governmental bodies. The mayor of the city of Jacksonville has recently requested that the authority temporarily suspend its future "expressway planning" until certain studies are completed by the Jacksonville Area Planning Board and the Florida Department of Transportation so that all of these bodies may coordinate their findings, and arrive at a comprehensive plan acceptable to all elements of Jacksonville society.

Accordingly, it is expected that the authority will adopt a resolution today suspending its expansion studies until the Department of Transportation data and reports are available and then resumption of studies can be undertaken. However, as a *Florida Times-Union* editorial over a year ago pointed out in congratulating this authority for commencing its future growth planning before it was too late, it is seven years lag-time from the first lines on a drawing board to the first automobile driving over the concrete of a new highway system. In the last ten years the number of registered vehicles in Duval County has increased by 60 per cent and many areas of the present expressway system are already at traffic levels which every expert agrees are well above capacity. Accordingly, any extensive delay in planning at this time by the Expressway Authority would be an abdication of responsibility to the public. Therefore, the authority urges the other agencies involved to complete their studies, some of which have already been in progress for over two years, without any avoidable delay, so that preparations and plans against future strangulation by traffic congestion can be under way by no later than the summer of 1971.

Roger L. Main
Chairman

The following letter was directed to Mayor Hans G. Tanzler, Jr.

November 18, 1970

The Honorable Hans G. Tanzler, Jr.
Mayor, City of Jacksonville
14th Floor, City Hall
Jacksonville, Florida 32202

Dear Mayor Tanzler:

This letter is in reply to your letter of October 15, 1970 to Mr. Roger L. Main, Chairman, Jacksonville Expressway Authority, with an attached copy of a report from the Jacksonville Area Planning Board wherein they have sought to evaluate the preliminary proposed new corridors for the expansion of the existing Jacksonville expressway system.

Please recall that the letter dated July 31, 1969 to you was accompanied by a resolution proposed by Mr. Richard J. Lewinson and unanimously adopted by the authority which covered and authorized preliminary engineering studies for proposed alignments for a future expanded expressway system that would best serve the people of Duval County. The Jacksonville Expressway Authority has always been cognizant of the ever increasing traffic flow being carried by the existing expressway system. This is vividly demonstrated by the increasing traffic passing through the toll facilities of the existing expressway system as well as traffic bottlenecks now existing.

These conditions are real today and do not require any expert to point out that relief should be given in the very near future at the following points.

1. At this time there is a dire need to eliminate the bottleneck where traffic from Roosevelt Boulevard (U.S. 17) merges with traffic from Interstate 10. Just to the east of this merger point traffic counts by the State Department of Transportation for the year of 1968-1969 indicated an average daily traffic count of 99,286. This point is just west of Stockton Street on Interstate 10.

2. Traffic now crossing the Fuller Warren Bridge has reached a point far in excess of that which should be carried by a four lane toll facility. The State Road Department of Transportation figures give an average of 42,400 vehicles crossing this bridge during the year of 1968-1969. Recent figures from July 29, 1970 through September 30, 1970 show that the average volume of traffic per day on Monday through Friday averages 52,060 cars per day. It is evident that relief is needed on this bridge and that other means of crossing the river should be provided.

3. The eight lane structure on the southside overcrossing the Florida East Coast properties lying to the east of Old Kings Road was crossed by an average of 83,812 cars per day during the fiscal year of 1968-1969, an increase of 21.7 per cent over the fiscal year of 1964-1965. The situation is approaching a critical point due to lane changing and crossover traffic movements. Traffic heading north or northwest, coming from Atlantic Boulevard, Interstate 95 and Philips Highway, creates this weaving condition inasmuch as their destination has to be the Main Street Bridge, the Acosta Bridge or the Fuller Warren Bridge. The reverse movement in the evening is equally bad. A

glimpse into the future will indicate what is in store for the public endeavoring to cross the St. Johns River by way of the above three bridges.

For example, when the Acosta Bridge was closed to traffic from March 10, 1970 through April 12, 1970 the average daily traffic crossing the Fuller Warren Bridge on Mondays through Fridays was 58,000 vehicles. The peak volume was 69,252 on Friday, April 13, 1970. During this period traffic was slowed to a standstill and was backed up for long distances on both sides of the approaches to the Fuller Warren Bridge. The backup also affected the traffic going to and from the Main Street Bridge.

4. Traffic on the Mathews Bridge has increased steadily during the past decade increasing from an average daily traffic load of 25,900 vehicles in 1961-1962 to 36,720 during 1969-1970. Traffic counts from the State Department of Transportation for the period of June 29, 1970 through September 30, 1970 for traffic on Mondays through Fridays give a figure of 42,219 vehicles per day. High day during this period was on March 20, 1970 totaling 47,090 cars.

Relative to the traffic over the Fuller Warren and John E. Mathews bridges an excerpt from the May 22, 1956 Report on Estimated Bridge Traffic and Revenue Tolls for the Jacksonville Expressway Authority by Coverdale & Colpitts, Consulting Traffic Engineers, New York City, on page 25 is as follows:

"Experience shows that when traffic on a four-lane urban toll bridge grows beyond 30,000 per day, the bridge becomes crowded in rush hours. For this reason lower growth rates for the five years starting in 1964 and an even lower rate (2.0 percent) thereafter until each bridge reaches an average daily traffic volume of 40,000 vehicles. At this level congestion in rush hours would become a serious problem and further growth would be very slow."

The construction of the Hart Bridge temporarily halted the rise in the growth pattern of traffic on the Mathews Bridge but now this has ceased and again the increase in traffic over the Mathews Bridge has begun to rise at a steady rate. The imminent growth of various sections within the Arlington area and east of the Arlington area will naturally increase the traffic on the Mathews Bridge. These facts are self-evident to those who use the Mathews Bridge and are acquainted with the growth of the Arlington area in general.

5. The traffic on Interstate 95 has shown a steady and phenomenal increase since it was opened in the early '60s. For example at 6th Street

the traffic in 1961-1962 was 54,269 whereas in 1968-1969 it was 78,803, an increase of 45 per cent. On Interstate 95 at 13th Street the traffic count in 1961-1962 was 47,924 and in 1968-1969 it was 74,065, an increase of 54.4 per cent.

Again on Interstate 95 at 26th Street the average daily traffic in 1961-1962 was 37,726 whereas in 1968-1969 the average daily traffic was 59,561, an increase of 58 per cent.

Also on the 20th Street expressway just east of Interstate 95 the average volume per day was 33,857 during the period of 1964-1965 and in 1968-1969 the average daily traffic was 43,591.

All of the above figures are from traffic counts obtained from the State Department of Transportation.

The above traffic data has been available to the authority and its engineers and it does not take any expert to evaluate the conditions as existing today other than knowing that the above points or corridors of travel should be given attention, and that plans should be developed to eliminate the critical points enumerated above. Such studies are being made by the authority's consulting engineers.

The Jacksonville Expressway Authority selected the consulting engineering firm of Sverdrup & Parcel and Associates, Inc., to make studies of corridors on the north and east sides of the river and the consulting engineering firm of Reynolds, Smith and Hills was designated to make studies of corridors to serve and connect to the expressway system on the north side of the river to connect to Interstate 295 in the Mandarin area. They were instructed to closely coordinate their thinking with the city of Jacksonville, the Jacksonville Duval County Planning Board and the Department of Transportation of the State of Florida, the Jacksonville Chamber of Commerce and other bodies public and private having interest in planning.

The above engineers have been carrying out their instructions as is evidenced by the numerous and various conferences they have had with many agencies of the city and groups of private citizens. All of the preliminary and investigative works of these firms of engineers have been made available to the Jacksonville Area Planning Board personnel.

The authority's engineers have been conscious of the need to recognize alignments as they may affect residential areas, businesses, schools, churches and other physical factors that would have to do with the lives of people. It is an established fact also that any new system of expressways and limited access facilities contemplated in an already built up community will inevitably involve the moving of some houses and businesses.

Our engineers are fully aware of the problems of pollution and ecology. One of the benefits of a limited access facility is a great reduction in pollution due to the average velocity of vehicles being over 40 miles per hour. It has been established scientifically that cars stopping and starting or slowing down to a crawl at traffic lights or at bridge approaches produce the greatest volume of air pollution.

As an example, the proposed alignment of an expressway through the Arlington area, through the central business district of Jacksonville and westward to a proposed connection to Interstate 295 will help reduce air pollution to a great extent. Traffic originating east of the St. Johns River in the Arlington area whose destination to the west or north or southwest of the central business district of Jacksonville could utilize the new proposed facility without having to cross city streets of the central business district. This route would also allow those who desire to enter the central business district to so do.

From this east-west alignment a new corridor is being proposed where traffic will be able to move to the southwest part of the city in the vicinity of Blanding Boulevard, Roosevelt Boulevard and Park Street. This proposed southwest connector is designated to relieve the terrible conditions now existing at the junction of interstate 10 and U.S. 17.

The consulting engineers also contemplate tying in the southwest alignment and west alignment to make a connection with the proposed river crossing adjacent to and just north of the Acosta Bridge. Connections are contemplated to this proposed new river crossing to serve the Riverside area with connections at Park Street and Jackson Street. These connections to the southwest and west of the city will greatly alleviate the heavy traffic load now being experienced by the Fuller Warren Bridge.

It is also suggested by the authority's consulting engineers that elevated facilities could be constructed on both sides of Interstate 95 to connect to the already discussed alignments wherein Interstate 95 would be improved northerly to a point some distance north of Golfair Boulevard.

The suggested alignment for a southside expressway which would pick up traffic from the Riverside area, the area west of the city of Jacksonville and downtown Jacksonville, would terminate at St. Augustine Road near Interstate 295. In so doing the alignment would have connections with Emerson Street, Old St. Augustine Road, University Boulevard, Powers Avenue near the junction of Old Kings Road, Baymeadows Road and Sunbeam Road. The purpose of this study is the anticipation of a substantial growth in the Mandarin-Loretto-St. Johns County area. Most of this traffic now must reach downtown Jacksonville or pass through Jacksonville by way of the eight lane structure previously mentioned. A comment by the Planning Board relative to the so-called downtown Mandarin alignment states as follows:

"From the information made available from the D.O.T. it does not appear that this route relates to any existing or future demands in the area. Map #6 shows the origin and destination desires and daily volume of trips in the city, as related to this area. Of the 23,780 A.D.T. crossing the St. Johns River, only 9,500 are to and from C.B.D. I-295, when in operation, will probably carry most of the through trips and other local trips across the river, not associated with C.B.D. For the remaining trips, presently, there are four major North-South traffic routes, i.e., I-95, Philips Highway (U.S. 1), San Jose Boulevard (S.R. 13) and Old St. Augustine Road. All of these are currently carrying 76,200 A.D.T. south of Emerson Street. Projections for 1990 indicate that the total traffic on all these routes will be 80,000 A.D.T. The routes have a combined capacity of 120,000 A.D.T., which can provide adequately for the projected needs."

Unfortunately, the writer of this paragraph evidently does not know that the traffic from Interstate 95 and Philips Highway converges on the eight lane structure which also has to take care of the traffic movements to and from Atlantic Boulevard. Further, the figures in the above quoted paragraph are given for points to the south of Emerson Street.

None of the proposed alignments for future expressways as now being proposed cut off any school zones as ample overcrossings are contemplated for the movement of people to and from both sides of the alignments. Another comment by the Planning Board is as follows:

"All available information indicates that this route is not needed. Any new bridge located adjacent to the Acosta Bridge should relate to the C.B.D. and relieve the congestion at Riverside Avenue."

Evidently the writer of this paragraph did not consult with the firm of Sverdrup & Parcel and Associates, Inc., to ascertain the manner in which they are contemplating the connection to this proposed river crossing to the Riverside area.

The expansion plans of the engineering consultants for the authority are based upon traffic conditions which now exist. Key traffic volumes at sections within the Riverside interchange have been projected to 1988 by the State Department of Transportation. These expansion figures were given to Sverdrup & Parcel by the State Department of Transportation on July 16, 1968 and form the bases for much of the projected future needs excepting only the Arlington area. The state projected average daily traffic on Interstate 10 just west of Stockholm Street for 1978 is 136,800 and for 1988 to be 185,600. The 1968 count was 99,286.

At the west end of the Warren Toll Bridge in Riverside, traffic projected for 1978 is 86,300 and for 1988 as 113,400. In 1968 the actual traffic movement was 42,400.

On Interstate 95 at Forest Street, the state projected traffic for 1978 is 130,700 and for 1988 as 174,600, whereas the actual count in 1968 was 81,723.

The above figures contradict the allegations made in the Planning Board remarks wherein they stated that "these routes are primarily based on a 'streets and highway plan for Duval County' published by the (then) State Road Department in 1960, rather than the Plan-1990 prepared by the Area Planning Board."

As to the proposed 1990 plan of the Jacksonville Area Planning Board, an inspection will reveal that there is not one single project indicated on the plan which would relieve any of the existing critical sections on the Jacksonville expressway system.

Furthermore, a crossing of the St. Johns River is indicated from the Arlington area from the vicinity of Fort Caroline Road to connect to the existing expressway system at 20th Street. If such an expressway were to be constructed an estimated 30,000 to 40,000 cars per day would eventually be thrown on that existing four lane expressway which now carries an average of 40,000 cars per day. If the four lanes were to be increased to eight lanes then traffic would be funneled to an already overtaxed interchange at Interstate 95. This certainly is not what a registered professional engineer would recognize as good highway planning. This proposed 20th Street route by the Planning Board extends easterly to follow McCormick Road into the Mayport area to form a connection to State Road A1A. This 20th Street plan does not show any major connections to Atlantic Boulevard that would siphon off traffic from the Regency Square area other than that where it intersects with a proposed easterly bypass.

Again, from the review by the City Planning Board to quote:

"Opening up of new areas, made accessible by the new routes, creates new subdivisions and new suburbs. Moreover, availability of sufficient cheap land with good accessibility tempts many manufacturing and business establishments to relocate out to new locations, completely changing the land use patterns, urban form, employment pattern, population distribution and social organization in the urban area."

The implication here is that no new roads whether expressway, limited access or mass transit facilities should be contemplated or constructed in the future inasmuch as it is alleged that such would completely change the land use patterns. It has been general knowledge for 25 to 30 years that the greatest residential growth patterns with their satellite business areas will be in the east and southeast parts of Duval County. The growth patterns of Duval County have been known and established for many years, particularly the vast industrial complexes in the northwest quadrant of Duval County as well as the northeast quadrant adjacent to and contiguous to the St. Johns River. It has also been known for many years that the growth pattern in the southwest of Duval County has been defined since the establishment of the Jacksonville Naval Air Station and Cecil Field. These Naval facilities in themselves have determined the residential growth patterns which can only be extended southerly into Clay County. The growth patterns of Duval County have not changed appreciably as to residential areas, business areas and industrial areas for many years and any change will only be by expansion of these particular activities.

The office of the Jacksonville Expressway Authority has been in a position to observe the development of Duval County in all its phases for the past 15 years and due to this particular knowledge has been able to render a service to the people of this community and assist other agencies with construction of an expressway system second to none for an area the size of the city. The Expressway Authority is dedicated to continue to plan for the future and at all times it will continue to work with and solicit the aid of all bodies who are involved in the problems of transportation. This assurance is made to all interested citizens.

As to mass transportation and the need for a sophisticated rapid transit system, the authority is well aware of current thinking on this matter. As to what a sophisticated rapid transit system covers is a moot question which problem is being studied by the great cities of the country who number their population in many millions.

Mass transit could be a reality in any community including Duval County if the citizens could be induced to use buses which could use the existing expressway system or any projected mass transit system.

Your letter and the recommendations of the Planning Board to you was that expressway planning be delayed until the Jacksonville urban area transportation study be completed.

This matter was taken up at the regular meeting of the authority on Thursday, November 12, 1970.

A motion was made and unanimously adopted that as the authority must cooperate with the city, all expressway expansion studies now under way be suspended until such time as the transportation studies by the Florida Department of Transportation for Jacksonville are available.

Furthermore, you are requested to ask the Jacksonville Area Planning Board to give to the authority definite and precise recommendations as to alignments of limited access facilities. The recommendations can then be submitted to the authority's traffic engineers and a determination made if the projects can be financed.

Please remember the matter of financing is the final determining factor in the construction of transportation facilities. Certain criteria must be rigidly adhered to and at all times the present traffic volumes and projected traffic volumes must be sufficient to produce ample revenues to cover all construction costs and all the intricate phases inherent in revenue bond financing.

Very truly yours,

Arthur N. Sollee
Executive Director

An editorial in the November 16, 1970 *Jacksonville Journal* "Expressway Plans" had this to say in the last paragraph: "In view of the necessity of coordinating all plans, the request for a delay was correct. The Expressway Authority's recognition of this by halting its plans shows a high degree of cooperation and concern for its overall public responsibility. The next move is up to those who asked for the delay. It is for them to see that marking time does not result in permanent stagnation."

On December 1, 1970 there was a meeting between representatives of the Jacksonville Expressway Authority and Jacksonville Area Planning Board. Those attending were Chairman Roger Main, attorney Earl Hadlow and Arthur N. Sollee for JEA, chairman William Jackson and executive director Marvin Hill for JAPB and Raymond Duncan administrative aide to Mayor Hans Tanzler.

Hadlow told the group that the authority had no intention of abdicating its responsibility.

Hill said that a study of Jacksonville's transportation problems would not be completed for two years.

Main asked, "How long can we wait for this thing?"

The first progress report on the Jacksonville urban area transportation study being conducted by Harland Bartholomew and Associates of Memphis, Tennessee was given to the Jacksonville Expressway Authority by Joseph W. Guyton, associate partner of the firm at the authority's February 25, 1971 meeting.

Guyton informed the members the study was about 60 per cent complete. He also stated that a study of the location of possible new expressways would be completed about January and the entire report would be completed in written form June, 1972.

At a regular meeting of the Technical Coordinating Committee held Tuesday, October 1971, Marvin Hill, committee chairman, told the committee the Florida Department of Transportation and the city of Jacksonville were bringing their transportation planning program up to date, reflecting anticipated needs through the year 1990. Hill said the process of re-evaluation will not be limited solely to highways, although that is presently the predominant method of transportation.

The Technical Coordinating Committee is composed of planners of the area planning board, the Jacksonville Transportation Authority, the city of Jacksonville, State Department of Transportation, representatives from St. Johns and Clay counties, Jacksonville Beach, Neptune Beach and town of Orange Park.

The Harland Bartholomew firm made its second appearance before the JTA on November 29, 1971. The firm's representative Joe Guyton said that the urban area transportation study, which they were doing, which had been under way since 1968, used previous studies, including the Jacksonville Area Planning Board's land use study, to come up with predictions for the need for six new bridges. Guyton said the 1990 projections were obtained on the basis of a population of over 900,000.

The next day Guyton and Paul Howard, another representative of the Bartholomew firm conferred with the Technical Coordinating Committee in the courthouse and requested help deciding the exact location of new bridges across the St. Johns River.

On January 25, 1972, Howard reported again to the Technical Coordinating Committee saying that motorists in 1990 may have a choice of five additional bridges to use when crossing the St. Johns River, if the highway transportation study being conducted by his firm for the State Department of Transportation is carried through to construction. He said the study would lead to a plan that would be ready for further study in June. The committee approved the plan for further study.

The Jacksonville Transportation Authority got into action at the meeting on March 21, 1972 by approving the extension of J. Turner Butler Boulevard from the University of North Florida site easterly to Jacksonville Beach less than a quarter of a mile north of the Duval-St. Johns County line. It was pointed out by Arthur N. Sollee that planning for the Butler extension went back 40 years. At that time the location was known as the Hogan Road extension.

For the remainder of 1972 Harland Bartholomew reported every month to the Technical Coordinating Committee on progress being made on the Jacksonville urban area transportation study. Arthur Sollee was the only member of the committee to vote "no" for the approval of the study for the following reasons:

1.   The River Oaks freeway, beginning in the Chaseville area in Arlington at University Boulevard North would cross Arlington River and go southerly to Interstate 95 just south of Emerson Street, then it would extend westerly to St. Johns River, thence cross the river to a point on west bank just west of Avondale, thence northwesterly to Roosevelt Boulevard.

      This location on the east side of the St. Johns River would go through apartment complexes, residential areas of high density and split the Granada area. In addition an interchange with I-95 would break all the rules of traffic engineering.

      The location on the west side of the river would cut through one of the most desirable and costly areas in the city. And interchanges at Boone Park and Park Street and at Roosevelt Boulevard would destroy an entire neighborhood and a large segment of the park.

2.   The Riverside freeway would start at Interstate 295, go north through the Confederate Point area and apartments, cross McGirts Creek, go through Lake Shore with an interchange at Blanding Boulevard destroying churches in so doing, would swing northwesterly close to Lee High School, then to form an interchange at Park Street with the proposed River Oaks Freeway, then north through numerous densely populated areas to a connection at Edgewood Avenue near Moncrief Road.

3.   The San Jose freeway section along Ft. Caroline Road westerly across the St. Johns River was impractical from the beginning, as the river crossing had been rejected by the U.S. Corps of Engineers in 1959.

4.   The Commodore Point freeway where it interchanged with the River Oaks Freeway between Atlantic Boulevard and Beach Boulevard, eliminates homes, apartments and businesses. Also, the interchange with Southside Boulevard would again destroy a vast number of homes.

The reader at this time should be reminded that at a meeting in the city on Thursday, July 3, 1970, Marvin Hill, executive director, Jacksonville Area Planning Board, said he was worried about Arlington's fate with an expressway (suggested by the Jacksonville Expressway Authority) through its center. "If it goes right through this community, it would violate the concept of the residential community." Donald E. Hunter of Marcou, O'Leary and Associates, the city's urban renewal consultants for the Eastside, estimated that as many as 500 to 550 housing units would be destroyed by the (JEA) route.

Yet both Hill and Hunter approved the 1990 Plan, truly a high point in inconsistency.

During the year of 1973 the reportable activities of the urban area transportation study were limited to a May 29th meeting of the Policy Committee of the Jacksonville Area Planning Board at which time it approved the recommended overall highway plan, previously approved by the board's technical coordinating committee.

Only Downtown Development Authority Chairman Homer Humphries registered his disapproval. He said he did not agree with plans to build three highways in the city's southwest through some of Jacksonville's finest and oldest residential areas. He further added he objected to the construction of River Oaks freeway and bridge, Timuquana Road and bridge and Riverside freeway which would create six interchanges between St. Johns Avenue and where the Timuquana Road bridge would intersect Roosevelt Boulevard.

On Wednesday April 3, 1974 Stephen Tocknell, an associate planner with the Jacksonville Area Planning Board spoke before nearly 200 persons of the Riverside Avondale Preservation group, in the Garden Club of Jacksonville, about the Riverside Freeway and the River Oaks Freeway which had been tentatively planned for the area. Tocknell maintained, though, that an effective mass transit system along either Post or College Streets would be more feasible than building freeways.

Culminating studies that began in 1967, the Jacksonville urban area transportation study was adopted as the basic plan that would govern U.S. Department of Transportation funding in the coming year. This was done, according to a news story in the June 26, 1974 issue of the *Jacksonville Journal* "with virtually no public attention."

The City Council Urban Affairs Committee in a move that would take the 1990 Jacksonville urban area transportation plan to the public throughout the city, assigned Councilman Lynwood Roberts to conduct public hearings.

Beginning November 21, 1974 and ending February 18, 1975 public hearings were held at the following places: Arlington Junior High School, Lee High School, Kissling Auditorium at the Riverside-Avondale Presbyterian Church, Wolfson

High School, Jackson High School, White High School, San Mateo Community School, Northwestern Junior High School and Mandarin Civic Center.

Councilman Roberts performed admirably in his efforts to present the 1990 plan. His most trying experience was at the January 20, 1975 hearing in Kissling Auditorium where the overflow crowd of about 500 Avondale and Riverside residents were unanimous in their opposition to any plan to build expressways or other major highways in their area.

Councilman Julian Fant, the representative of the area stated "The Riverside freeway will not become a reality."

The absolute folly and uselessness, in having Councilman Roberts waste his time and the public's in conducting the eight public hearings began to manifest itself, when the jam-packed auditorium heard Arthur Sollee read from the approved five-year short range plan that the Riverside, Fort Caroline, and Commodore Point freeways, the River Oaks and Timuquana bridges and the 20th Street extension, which were in the original Jacksonville urban area study completed in 1970, were deleted for at least five years.

The crowd became fully convinced as to the utter futility of all the hearings, when they listened to Jacksonville Area Planning Board Executive Director Ed Baker and assistant planner Steve Tocknell tell them the city planners are "starting from scratch with a new Jacksonville urban area study update in which there are no proposals that must be accepted."

Councilman Roberts further completed the obituary when he said, "These roads are not in the five-year plan, and as far as them ever materializing, I don't think they will."

The chronological order of events has been used to illustrate the great length of time that has passed since Mayor Hans Tanzler requested the Jacksonville Transportation Authority to cease planning.

Sad to say, not a single grain of sand or a cubic yard of concrete nor a pound of steel has gone into any of the plans that were proposed by the Jacksonville Area Planning Board, its battery of consultants and the mayor.

What has gone on this past decade is a lesson in futility and utter frustration for those who have suffered through such an experience. During this period, the Jacksonville area transportation study has cost well over a million dollars.

It should be a striking lesson to all public officials that the planning, design, construction and supervision of all public works should be by registered and experienced professionals.

Quite apropos to the subject, speaking to transportation experts attending a University of North Florida seminar, on October 12, 1973, General John P. Doyle of Texas A & M University declared "Planning without implementation is a waste and a fraud."

Again I wish to quote from an editorial in the November 16, 1970 *Jacksonville Journal* when it commented on Mayor Hans Tanzler's request to the Jacksonville Expressway Authority to cease planning. "The next move is up to those who asked for the delay. It is for them to see that marking time does not result in permanent stagnation."

The operations of the Jacksonville Transportation Authority since consolidation have been infused with many politically oriented problems which have lessened the ability of the authority to efficiently carry out its original concepts.

A warning as to such a problem was issued in the report of the Jacksonville Expressway Authority for the fiscal year, ended June 30, 1960 by Lucius A. Buck, authority chairman when he wrote:

"This authority has, through its life, been administered as a public business. Politics have been avoided. Pressures for special consideration, for political decisions, and for political appointments have been firmly resisted. The members of the authority have sought to maintain its activities on the high plane of dedicated public service. Economy, the establishment and maintenance of sound credit, and high quality construction have been the goals of the authority and those goals have been very largely achieved. So long as membership on this authority is looked upon as a matter of community service and so long as the sole guiding principle is public service these goals can continue to be realized. If, however, the authority should ever become a political football, or resort to appointments on the basis of political considerations rather than merit and actual need, or bow to pressure groups and special interests, its ability to contribute to the welfare of this community will be dubious."

It is now up to the public to act.

Note: The Jacksonville Expressway Authority became the Jacksonville Transportation Authority on June 4, 1971.

FEDERAL BUREAU OF PUBLIC ROADS

Today men still live who remember when a hamlet, a village, a town, a city, a county or even a state controlled its own destiny. They can reminisce for hours, extolling the virtues of the particular methods by which they solved the common problems of their day. And, with a gleam in their eye, they emphasize they depended on no one other than themselves for community needs.

Such men were reliant and fierce in the defense of their right to find ways and means to govern and be governed by the rules and regulations that would be compatible with their own particular needs and way of life.

But today— what a contrast! The benevolent laws of yesteryear have been superseded by thousands of confusing laws conceived in the theoretically oriented minds of countless would-be solons. Such thinking has infiltrated and permeated far too many of the established bureaucracies so that today we are swamped with a multiplicity of regulations and directives that are often interpreted and enforced by opinionated individuals who by reason of their appointed positions issue edicts with the haughty domineering spirit of absolute monarchs of a thousand years ago.

Fortunately, in contrast, there still remain a few who continue firm in their belief it is the people who should govern. Fortunately, too, such men do manage to remain within established bureaucracies and cry out their warnings even if the battles are not always won.

One of these bureaucracies, the Federal Bureau of Public Roads, an arm of the U.S. Department of Commerce, for generations has been a gigantic force in the developing of the nation's integrated system of highways. Its rigid rules and regulations have encompassed every facet in the field of road and bridge building. Until about 1957 the participation of the federal government in the state's road building programs was rather a "matter of course" procedure. It was accepted with the enthusiasm of a "shotgun marriage" and has continued to live and survive.

The Federal-Aid Highway Act of 1956 declared it was most essential to the national interest to provide for the early completion of the "national system of interstate highways" and because of its primary importance to the national defense, changed the name of the system to the "national system of interstate and defense highways." The "act" further declared that such system in the future be referred to as the "interstate system."

The new program began with the issuance of circular policy and procedure memorandums and general administrative memorandums, each of which was superseded from week to week and month-to-month by new ones. These change-of-mind policies by the top echelon made it so difficult for the "grass roots" personnel to properly function, that it was a source of embarrassment to them when asked as to what procedures should be followed in the acquisition of rights of way for the interstate system. Their answers were, "The regulations this week say do this, but next week we hear there will be changes made— so let's wait."

The procrastinations of the bureau in its policy decisions pertaining to the acquisition of rights of way so exhausted the patience of the Jacksonville Expressway Authority and the State Road Department, that a memorandum agreement as of January 31, 1958 was entered into by both parties which had the effect of increasing the department's pledge from $17,121,000 to approximately $22,000,000 on the basis of estimated construction costs. The agreement was captioned as follows:

> Memorandum of procedures to be followed by the Jacksonville Expressway Authority and the State Road Department from February 1st, 1958, in the acquisition of rights of way and construction of Jacksonville expressway system.

> Paragraph 2 of the memorandum is quoted as it appeared on page 14 of Jacksonville Expressway Authority, Report, for fiscal year ending June 30, 1958.

> The department and the authority are in agreement that the attempted qualification of rights of way acquisitions as federal aid projects has proved highly unsatisfactory in that increased costs and delays have occurred, and the department has not been reimbursed by the Federal Bureau of Public Roads on a single such project. In an effort to eliminate further delays and to avoid increased costs, it is agreed that the authority will proceed to acquire with bond funds all additional rights of way for the north-south route and for the west route (as those routes are determined, approved and scheduled by the authority).

The memorandum covered 12 paragraphs and was signed by Lucius A. Buck, chairman, Jacksonville Expressway Authority and by Wilbur E. Jones, chairman, State Road Department.

Although the above action by the authority expedited by years the completion of the 1957 revenue bond program, it never did succeed in convincing the bureau's engineers that many of the interchanges should be designed and constructed from a practical point of view and not based upon pure theory. If the foresightedness of the authority had been followed, then today the traveling public would not have to contend with the left turn movements at the intersections of Interstate 95 with Dunn Avenue, Golfair Boulevard, and 20th Street; also, Interstate 10 with McDuff Avenue; Cassat Avenue, and Lane Avenue.

In the early months of 1961 the State Road Department and federal government began to consider the extension of Interstate 95 from the existing terminus at Philips Highway, southerly to the St. Johns County line. The authority was informed of their thinking as to alignments and designs. After receiving such information, the S.R.D. district engineer was advised as follows:

March 1, 1962

Mr. J.A. Brewer, District Engineer
State Road Department
Lake City, Florida

Dear Mr. Brewer:

In view of the fact that the State Road Department has established an office in Jacksonville for the purpose of acquiring rights of way for Interstate 95 from the Jacksonville expressway south to the St. Johns County line, I wish to inquire as to the type of interchange that is being proposed at Love Grove Road. The preliminary rights of way maps of Interstate 95 which your office let me have are not clear as to details which, for many reasons, is understandable. You are aware of the large volume of traffic that is using Love Grove Road and each year the count is skyrocketing. One thing is certain, and that is that a diamond interchange at Love Grove Road and Interstate 95 would be a disaster. A study of existing conditions of this area and a projection of the growth that is inevitable will clearly indicate that any type of interchange other than a diamond can be justified.

Very truly yours,

Arthur N. Sollee
Executive Director

Note: Love Grove Road is now University Boulevard West

Later Brewer stated he had contacted a representative of the bureau about the matter but "it was like talking to a brick wall and there was nothing that he could do about it."

During the next several months I had the opportunity to talk with personnel from the bureau's Tallahassee office concerning the thinking that was being used in arriving at the final design phases of Interstate roads in Duval County. One of the representatives, Francis D. Pryor, division appraiser of the bureau went beyond his sphere of duties and by memorandum to W.C. Peterson, bureau division engineer, Tallahassee, Florida gave him the facts about what was going on in Duval County covering apparent inadequacies in the design of interchanges where interstate roads intersected existing heavily traveled state and federal roads. Pryor also talked to Gordon H. Sirmans, bureau area engineer about the matter.

On numerous occasions I had lengthy discussions with Sirmans covering the design and construction of interstate road interchanges. When it appeared Sirmans was rather fixed in his thinking, as a last resort, the following written appeal was sent to him.

3635 University Boulevard South
Jacksonville, Florida
April 4, 1963

Mr. Gordon H. Sirmans
2016 Dellwood Drive
Tallahassee, Florida

Dear Gordon:

Just this past week I was shown Pages 20 and 21 of State Road 9, Florida Interstate 95, Section 72280-2401, Duval County, Florida, on which sheets were indicated the property needed for rights of way at the intersection of Patton Drive and Emerson Street with Interstate 95.

You will recall that I have discussed this matter with you, and you are very familiar with the fact that I am absolutely opposed to diamond interchanges being constructed where major arterial highways of high traffic volume cross major expressways. This letter is being sent to your home address inasmuch as it is not to be considered as an official document but is purely a friendly letter to you as an engineer and from me as a resident of Duval County who has seen many terrible blunders made in the past, particularly where proper interchanges were not built at major highway crossings.

I am attaching copies of newspaper clippings having reference to a diamond interchange at Chaseville Road (now University Boulevard) with the Arlington expressway. You will note the newspaper comments are not too complimentary. As a result of the inadequacy of this diamond interchange, the Expressway Authority had to spend $538,292 to construct a very tight cloverleaf interchange.

Several examples of bad judgment and poor planning are cited as follows:

1. The Gator Bowl interchange had to be reconstructed by the authority at the cost of $1,574,000.

2. The connection at U.S. 17 (Main Street North) with Imeson Airport had to be built by the authority at the cost of $1,027,084. This was made necessary on account of the left hand turn movement at the northern terminus of the expressway and known as the Heckscher Drive interchange with U.S. 17.

3. During the early 1950s and during the designing period for the original portion of the Jacksonville expressway, the office of the

county engineer made several suggestions to the State Road Department relative to the design of correct interchanges; particularly, a proper design was given the State Road Department for the intersection of Southside Boulevard and Beach Boulevard. A three-hour conference with one of the State Road Department engineers resulted in his determining that traffic counts did not warrant a full and complete interchange in this major intersection. He was told that he was being shortsighted but this proved to be of no avail with the result that:

At the present time, the so-called interchange of Southside Boulevard (U.S. Alt 1) with Beach Boulevard (U.S. 90) is considered one of the great blunders and one of the poorest pieces of engineering in the state. If one had deliberately started out to design a bad intersection, he could not have succeeded any better. An on-the-sight inspection will verify these conditions.

Another interchange which has subsequently proved to not tie in with current conditions is the 20th Street interchange with Interstate 95. Although the 20th Street route was known to be a part of the expressway system, the southeast quadrant of this intersection did not call for a cloverleaf and today would not come under the requirements of the Bureau of Public Roads, if 20th Street were to be designated a federal route.

The existing diamond interchanges at 8th Street and Golfair Boulevard with Interstate 95 are fairly adequate today but the time is fast approaching where there will be trouble with the left hand turn movements.

Tentative data which I have every reason to believe will be incorporated in Volume 2 of the Jacksonville-Duval County Transportation Study being made by the State Road Department specifically points out that on the present systems of roads in Duval County, left hand turns from arterials should be prohibited.

Several months ago at one of the joint meetings of the Highway Committee of the Jacksonville Chamber of Commerce with personnel from the State Road Department, a statement was made by the representative of the State Road Department that the intersection of Roosevelt Boulevard (U.S. 17) with Timuquana Road was probably the worst left hand turn movement in the state of Florida.

Again, quoting from Volume 2 of the engineering study enumerated above and having reference to southern radial Interstate 95, it is stated that, "Approximately 2.9 mile section from Atlantic Boulevard to

University Boulevard will require six travel lanes to accommodate 60,000 vehicles per day for anticipated 1980 average daily traffic."

From the same report and having reference to Emerson Street expressway, to quote: "The anticipated 1980 daily travel of approximately 40,000 vehicles from the section from Main Street (expressway) for approximately 4.2 miles to Arlington freeway will require six travel lanes."

Plans of the Jacksonville Expressway Authority call for the construction of what is known as the "Commodore Point project." It is contemplated that there will be an interchange at Beach Boulevard a few hundred feet westerly of Highland Avenue, with a cloverleaf design at this intersection. A stub will be left so that within a relatively short period, a limited access connection can be made to intersect Spring Park Road at Emerson Street. This will be only a short distance easterly from the intersection of Interstate 95 and Emerson Street (see map). The program of the county, collaborating with the authority, calls for the paving of University Boulevard (formerly Love Grove Road) from San Jose Boulevard to the Arlington Expressway, the pavement to be a 64 ft. curb and gutter section calling for four travel lanes with parking on both sides. State Road Department traffic counts today show that over 10,000 cars pass daily over the existing two-lane facility where Interstate 95 will cross University Boulevard West.

I am enclosing a map on which is indicated in orange, the proposed Commodore Point Bridge project along with connecting roads. Please note also the county program in the area which is shown in red and orange. Emerson Street will be paved 64 ft. wide from curb to curb to tie into a comparable existing section between Philips Highway (U.S. 1) and Spring Park Road. Therefore, Emerson Street will be a major arterial highway, connecting the various points of southeast Duval County and the city of Jacksonville and it will be a major feeder from Interstate 95 to the easterly part of Jacksonville by way of the Commodore Point Bridge.

It is hoped that all of this data and information may be of some service to you so that in your official capacity, you may help in determining proper interchanges at Emerson Street and University Boulevard with Interstate 95 and under no circumstances construct a diamond or Texas type interchange at these two intersections. Again, please remember the blunders that had to be rectified at the University Boulevard-Arlington expressway and Gator Bowl intersections.

Thanks for anything that you may do to prevent the construction of two monstrosities.

Sincerely,

Arthur N. Sollee

Enclosures

The foregoing letter was ignored and Interstate 95 South was constructed with the interchanges standing as a lasting monument to misdirected federal bureaucracy.

As citizens began using the stretch of Interstate 95 from Bowden Road north to downtown Jacksonville, many became painfully aware that something was amiss at the Emerson Street, University Boulevard West and Bowden Road interchanges. Their first thoughts always seemed to turn to the Jacksonville Expressway Authority as being the one guilty of the errors. Gentle reprimands to downright abuse and ridicule were directed to authority personnel, who always had to explain that the U.S. Bureau of Public Roads was the culprit and not the authority.

The State Road Department engineers in Lake City, Florida were sympathetically aware of the situation, so when in January, 1966, they were visited by members of the Special Committee on the Federal-Aid Highway Program, they suggested the members confer with the authority relative to highway problems involving both bodies.

On January 27, 1966 Salvatore J. D'Amico, associate counsel and Paul R.S. Yates, professional staff member of the Special Subcommittee on the Federal-Aid Highway program, Committee on Public Works, House of Representatives, Washington, D.C. held a conference with me. Many facets of the interrelationship between the bureau and other governmental bodies involved in the construction of roads were discussed at length.

A few weeks later, I received a telephone call from D'Amico requesting what I had told him in Jacksonville be put in letter form. This was done on February 22, 1966.

February 22, 1966

Mr. Salvatore J. D'Amico
Associate Counsel
Special Subcommittee on the
Federal-Aid Highway Program
Committee on Public Works
B-376 Rayburn Building
House of Representatives
Washington 25, D.C.

Dear Mr. D'Amico:

When you and Mr. Yates were in my office on Thursday, January 27, 1966, we had a general discussion relative to the participation by the Bureau of Public Roads in the construction of highways in cities, counties and the states. You will remember that I stated most emphatically that one of the weak points in the construction of the interstate roads particularly in Duval County, was the construction of left turning movements at intersections with major highways.

As I recall you stated that one of the purposes of your visit was to ascertain in what manner the Bureau of Public Roads could better serve and construct these highway networks in cooperation with the various communities. You also will recall I stated if a local community was in a position to finance its expressways and toll highways it should be allowed to do so inasmuch as the work could always be done within a definite and minimum length of time. It is realized that it would be impossible for the Bureau of Public Roads to specify such limitations on account of working with the State Road Departments who are not bound by limitations in their overall construction programs.

The Federal-Aid Highway Program in Duval County has contributed in a great degree to the success of the expressway system and this participation by the Bureau of Public Roads has been well received by the county inasmuch as it released certain bond funds that were used most advantageously in upgrading many elements of the system that were not on the federal-aid system. Subsequently, some of the routes have been designated as federal routes.

For your information I am sending to you excerpts from the Jacksonville-Duval County Transportation Study 1960, Volume II, Recommended Improvements prepared by Florida State Road Department in cooperation with Board of County Commissioners Duval County and the U.S. Department of Commerce, Bureau of Public Roads. On Page 31 of the above report under South Radial I-95, it is stated that "the approximately 2.9 mile section from Atlantic Boulevard (freeway) to University Boulevard will require six travel lanes to accommodate 60,000 vehicles per day that the anticipated 1980 A.D.T." On Page 34 of this same report under the heading Emerson Street Expressway, it states that "the anticipated 1980 A.D.T. of approximately 40,000 vehicles per day for the section from Main Street (expressway) 4.2 miles to Arlington freeway will require six travel lanes."

Attached to this report are aerial photographs recently made which indicate the type of interchanges constructed at Emerson Street and I-

95 and at University Boulevard West and Interstate 95. Please note the design of these two interchanges which are supposedly based upon the anticipated average daily traffic movements previously cited. The point is why spend tens of thousands of dollars on transportation studies if the recommendations are not followed at least at points so glaring as the Emerson Street-I-95 intersection?

In Chapter 9, "Grade Separations and Interchanges," as noted in a publication entitled "A Policy on Geometric Design of Rural Highways" by American Association of State Highway Officials, are certain paragraphs from which I would like to quote.

On page 366 of this chapter it is stated, "The diamond or parallel ramp type of interchange has four one-way ramps. It is especially adaptable to **major-minor** highway intersections with limited right of way. . .The acceptability of the diamond type interchange is dependent largely upon the capacity of the minor road, particularly at the ramp terminals."

On Page 369 in the aforesaid Chapter 9, I quote: "Right turning movements at interchanges follow simple direct or nearly direct paths on which there is little possibility of driver confusion. Cloverleaf interchanges require loop paths for the left turning movements, maneuvers that confuse many drivers and require added travel distance. The diamond pattern of ramps is simple for the driver and is more adaptable than a cloverleaf in cases where **direct left turns are fitting on the minor road**. But where traffic on the minor road is sufficient to justify the expenditure to eliminate the at-grade left turns, a **cloverleaf** or higher type interchange should be considered."

Continuing under the caption of "Safety," on Page 370, I quote: "All types of accidents are inherent to at-grade intersections, and they cannot be eliminated completely by design. A highway grade separation, on the other hand, eliminates all possibilities of accidents between the intersecting through movements. The limited widths at a structure result in some types of off-pavement accidents but these are minor compared to the likely vehicle-contact accidents to be expected without the highway grade separation. The provision of a complete interchange eliminates all crossing conflict between turning and through traffic, substituting instead the less hazardous merging and diverging movement. **The removal of the head-on conflict between the left turning movements and opposing through movements is especially conducive to lower accident rates.** Right turn traffic is safer also in that a higher type ramp connection is provided at an interchange than at an at-grade intersection."

At intersections with major streets and where traffic "backs up" during the morning and evening rush hours the factor of economy from the motorist's angle should be an important factor. Getting the most vehicles per minute through such busy interchanges will save thousands of dollars to the motorist. A design criteria should be Time=Money and when evaluated over a period of 20 to 30 years will-throw new light on the elements used in the design factors of interchanges.

Several years ago traffic officials in Houston, Texas, after carefully analyzing all factors affecting the character of traffic, estimated the value of time savings by passenger vehicles at two cents per minute, and commercial vehicles had a value of three cents per minute. This, in itself, offers some proof that a time equals money consideration is much in evidence.

There recently has been constructed in Duval County a major interchange at U.S. 301 and Interstate 10, a photograph of which is attached to illustrate existing conditions. Right turn off and on ramps could eliminate these dangerous left turning movements. This particular interchange was the subject of an editorial on a recent television broadcast which was not very flattering.

It is my understanding that the interstate is being constructed to last many years in the future and that its designs are supposed to incorporate features which will be most conducive to the safety of the traveling public. In Duval County conditions are such that they cannot be compared in general to areas in the Midwest and the central states for the population is increasing at a tremendous rate, all of which should be taken into consideration in the design and construction of every element of the interstate highways. For instance, I have already pointed out that, although a report which has been published and participated in by the Bureau of Public Roads gives a combined traffic load of 100,000 cars a day at the intersection of Emerson Street and I-95, left turn movements have been incorporated at this important intersection. In the opinion of many this is not just the thing that should have been done.

Please understand that the purpose of these statements is to bring to the attention of those concerned with a development of proper highways in this country that advance thinking should take precedent over small minor increases in the cost of construction. Any future improvements to these obsolete types of interchanges will cost many times that which they would have cost at the beginning of a construction program.

In my position as executive director I always hear from the general public when they think that some part of the expressway is in need of correction and I can certify that we are getting the blame for the inadequacies being built into these local interstate interchanges.

Further, the Jacksonville Expressway Authority cannot deal directly with Bureau of Public Roads and participation by the authority involving any federal highway must be channeled through the State Road Department.

The statements which I have made are my own personal views and in no way should they be construed to be those of the Jacksonville Expressway Authority.

Very truly yours,

Arthur N. Sollee
Executive Director

ANS:p
Attachments

After receiving the above letter, D'Amico made a follow-up telephone call asking if I would be willing to appear before the Special Subcommittee on the Federal-Aid Highway Program on March 17, 1966. To this I agreed.

The testimony which was given in the Rayburn Building, Washington, D.C. covered all of the items that were included in the February 22, 1966 letter to D'Amico. It is documented under the title "Relationship of Toll Facilities to the Federal-Aid Highway Program" and printed for the use of the Committee on Public Works by the U.S. Government Printing Office.

It should be very apparent to the people of Duval County and to the public in general that the Bureau of Public Roads again has turned deaf ears to the above suggestions when they get on and off Interstate 295 at State Road 13 in the Mandarin area, Blanding Boulevard (S.R. 21) and Roosevelt Boulevard (U.S. 17) at the Duval-Clay County line, and at Jacksonville Heights Road. The latest fiasco is the I-95 Butler Boulevard interchange.

No guesswork is needed to estimate what the traffic conditions will be in later years at the above interchanges. Signalization will help, but the slowing down and backing up of traffic will be perpetually frustrating and costly to the travelling public — truly a monument to bureaucratic ineptitude at such vital points in an otherwise magnificent system of roads.

Duval County Road Data - 1925 - 1945

TABLE SHOWING
ROAD AND BRIDGE EXPENDITURES FOR CONSTRUCTION
AND MAINTENANCE OF DUVAL COUNTY, FLA., ROADS
AND BRIDGES EXCLUSIVE OF BOND ISSUES AND OTHER COMPARATIVE
DATA FROM 1925 THROUGH 1945

1	2	3	4	5	6	7	8	9	10
Year	Road and Bridge Expenditures	Number Convict Laborers Available	Population of Duval County	Population Outside City of Jax.	Miles County Roads	Number of Motor Vehicles	Costs Per Capita	Costs Per Mile Road	Cost Per Motor Vehicle
1924-25	$356,110	107	123,481				2.97		
1925-26	304,926	127							
1926-27	540,614	169							
1927-28	574,596	180							
1928-29	601,533	182							
1929-30	599,580	162	155,503	25,954	588	38,319	3.80	$1004	$15.65
1930-31	577,127	186							
1931-32	414,936	153							
1932-33	131,720	163							
1933-34	133,339	187							
1934-35	147,696	242	175,204	28,945	689	39,190	0.84	214	3.77
1935-36	186,766	186							
1937-37	293,543	191							
1937-38	226,561	187							
1938-39	207,161	197							
1939-40	224,776	162	210,143	37,075	741	56,172	1.07	303	4.00
1940-41	163,958	175							
1941-42	277,508	178							
1942-43	183,072	119							
1943-44	174,869	94							
1944-45	218,462	103	272,449	66,007	781	58,200	0.81	280	3.75

TABULATION SHOWING AREA IN SQUARE MILES, POPULATION, OUTSIDE
THE CITY LIMITS OF JACKSONVILLE AND THE TOTAL NUMBER OF MILES
OF ROADS IN EACH COUNTY COMMISSIONER'S DISTRICT

AS OF NOVEMBER 10, 1945

District	*Area Square Mile	Per Cent. Area	Total All Roads Miles	Per-Cent Miles of Roads	1945 Population Outside of Jacksonville City Limits	Per-Cent Population
1	154	20.4	104	13.3	3632	5.5
2	50	6.6	103	13.2	7680	11.6
3	234	31.0	213	27.3	11,800	17.9
4	78	10.4	137	17.5	14,659	22.2
5	238	31.6	224	28.7	**28,236	48.8
Total	754	100.0	781	100.0	66,007	100.0

* Exclusive of Parts in City and in St. Johns River
** Includes 10,614 in 3 towns at Beaches

CHAPTER XXIX
THE PROPOSED DAMES POINT BRIDGE — PHASE ONE

It may surprise many to know that a proposed crossing from the Dames Point area to the south side of the St. Johns River dates back to the year of 1954.

Jospeh Crain a superb reporter assigned to the courthouse beat by *The Florida Times-Union*, contacted me daily due to my position as the county engineer. Our conversations invariably turned to the planning of roads and bridges and the economic potentials of Duval County. On several occasions I had mentioned the feasibility of Jacksonville as the hub of a vast transportation system linking the United States to South America. The system would consist of a sea-train from Jacksonville to Venezuela, from which would extend throughout all South American countries a vast network of railroads, highways and airports. This idea was covered in considerable detail by the *Jacksonville Journal*, February 2, 1945.

Over nine years later, on March 22, 1954 Crain came to my office and informed me that the idea of the Dames Point-Goat Island area being used as a northern terminus for a sea-train connection to South America was in jeopardy, the reason being a group of citizens headed by Judge Ollie Edmunds had applied to the State Internal Improvement Board for the purchase of the islands. He verified his statement by showing me the advertised legal application in the *Legal News*.

I contacted all of the County Commissioners at once, passing on to them the information given to me by Crain and suggested they should block the sale, as the lands in the future could be utilized for port facilities by the county or the city.

The next day, at their regular meeting, the commission voted unanimously to forestall the private acquisition of Terminal or Goat Island, Alligator Island and other lands in the St. Johns River north and northwest of the new Dames Point cutoff and south of the Eastport-New Berlin area.

The first time the public had any idea as to how Goat Island could be developed, was the published map of the area shown on page one of the October 29, 1955 *Jacksonville Journal*. (See copy of original map at the end of this chapter.) Also map showing southeast section of Duval County in 1955. A close inspection shows a possible location of an expressway from the Dames Point area crossing Goat Island and designated to go south to U.S. Highway 1.

The County Commission, after acquiring the islands by official act, later renamed the area as Blount Island, after J. Henry Blount, the highly respected county attorney.

In 1971 the Jacksonville Transportation Authority authorized their consulting engineers, Sverdrup and Parcel and Associates, Inc. to prepare cost estimates for an eastern bypass. The location as shown on the accompanying sketch indicates a river crossing east of Dames Point and Blount Island, the section south of the river following for several miles a 200 foot right of way which had previously been dedicated to the county for highway purposes at no cost. Sverdrup and Parcel submitted their report in November, 1971 but no action was taken by the authority.

In the meantime the authority had been caught up in the meshes of the 1990 Jacksonville Urban Area Transportation Study. So, any positive unilateral action on their part was completely out of the question.

From its beginning to its demise the Dames Point Bridge scenario could be taken from a quotation from Sheakespeare's "As You Like It" — "All the world's a stage, And all the men and women merely players. They have their exits and their entrances."

I have some reluctance in attempting to cover such a scenario, for the combined talents of writers from the daily press have given excellent coverage during the years that were devoted by public officials to construct a river crossing from Dames Point over Blount Island to the Arlington area.

The impasse was finally broken, for at the August 29, 1972 meeting of the JTA, a letter was received from Mayor Hans Tanzler in which he stated that inasmuch as the Jacksonville Transportation Authority had discontinued its studies at his request, he now would like to encourage the authority to again proceed to expedite the implementation of the construction of a bridge across the St. Johns River north of the Mathews Bridge.

Also, at this meeting, the authority received information that the Jacksonville Urban Area Transportation Study Policy Committee at their July 25th meeting, unanimously adopted a motion recommending to the authority that it proceed with a financial feasibility and/or location study of east-west and north-south river crossings in the corridors recommended by the Technical Coordinating Committee.

At the September 21st meeting of the JTA, the authority's Secretary Karl Ambrose offered a motion that a feasibility study be made of the Dames Point Bridge and the 20th Street crossing and that other projects be tabled until the feasibility was made. The authority voted unanimously for the motion.

Another positive step was taken to further the progress of the proposed bridge, when James D. Ward, the district two engineer for the Florida Department of Transportation called for the formation of a Public Participation Committee to work with Reynolds, Smith, & Hills, architects, engineers and planners on a 10-month study to determine the location of a proposed limited access highway to the bridge.

The first meeting of the committee was held in the offices of Reynolds, Smith & Hills on February 15, 1973 with Al R. Baxley an engineer with Reynolds, Smith & Hills presiding as chairman.

William W. Page, assistant district two planning engineer and project manager told the committee the location of Offshore Power Systems on Blount Island would make the construction of the highway one of the top priorities of the DOT and the JTA.

At the May 4th meeting of the Participation Committee, in response to a question concerning which portions of the route would be constructed first and whether the entire route would be built, Page explained that the Federal Highway Administration and the State DOT policies dictate that a logical beginning and terminus be studied. Those portions given a high priority would be built first and those portions not constructed would be studied again before being considered. A public hearing would be held whenever a change in the established route is to be considered. When questioned as to priorities, Page stated that during the study certain portions will be seen as high priorities, and DOT currently has programed in the five-year work program, improvements of the Arlington triangle and a section south of Beach Boulevard from J. Turner Butler Boulevard to Beach Boulevard.

Simultaneously with the meetings of the Public Participation Committee, the JTA was taking steps to finance the construction of the Dames Point Bridge, for at their July 17, 1973 meeting they voted unanimously to raise bridge tolls a dime to 25 cents for passenger cars and two-axle trucks, and to raise the toll for trucks with more than two axles proportionately to be effective on September 1.

Chairman Wesley C. Paxson of the JTA said the toll increase was necessary in order to sell $171 million in parity bonds for the construction of the Dames Point Bridge and the completion of the easterly extension of the J. Turner Butler Boulevard across the Intracoastal Waterway to the vicinity of Ponte Vedra Beach.

Almost immediately after the above action, members and personnel of the authority began to be the guest speakers of various civic organizations where they gave facts and figures as to why the Dames Point Bridge project should be built.

It was now the time for the tempo of the Dames Point Bridge drama to increase. The participants felt they had an eager and diversified listening public audience, so at every appearance they spoke their parts with the sincere belief that they were on the right side of a viable and just cause.

At a Northside Business Men's Club on September 11th at the Bonanza Sirloin Pit on Norwood Avenue, in answer to criticism by State Representative Carl Ogden, Authority Chairman Wesley Paxson charged that political interference was being injected into JTA efforts to boost bridge toll revenues for borrowing $171 million to build a Dames Point Bridge and a 14-mile expressway tying into Interstate 95.

The Florida legislative subcommittee on local toll problems met in Jacksonville on October 2nd in the courthouse for the purpose of studying how highway priorities are established by state and local transportation officials. The subcommittee was headed by Senator Bruce Smathers and included Representatives Eric Smith and Earl Dixon.

Representatives of the Jacksonville Area Planning Board, Walter Skinner the deputy district engineer from the State Department of Transportation and Edward Mueller, the Jacksonville Transportation Authority's executive director outlined the comlexities of planning and implementing highway projects.

Skinner told the committee it took a minimum of two years and up to four years on a U.S. highway funded project "before you can spend the first dollar" of federal funds.

Mueller told the committee the JTA had no project priorities, but had several projects in the implementation stages at one time. The reason for this was that one or more of the projects could be shelved for any number of reasons, including high cost, insurmountable environmental problems, and maritime considerations.

This statement by Mueller was in direct conflict with Chairman Paxsons's July 17th statement of selling $171 million in bonds to build the Dames Point Bridge.

At a JTA meeting held January 16, 1974 Chairman Wesley Paxson said that lower than anticipated revenue from the 25-cent toll would force the authority to lower next year's potential bond issue from $171 million to $149.5 million.

A public hearing was held by the State Department of Transportation on April 17th relative to the location of a proposed freeway linking the southern intersection of Interstates 295 and 95 with the northern intersection of the same two highways by way of the proposed Dames Point Bridge. At this hearing Captain Henry A. Steele, president of the St. Johns River Bar Pilots Association said that the planned 150 foot height of the bridge would choke off the city's vital shipping commerce. He said the Bar Pilots Association was exasperated at the apparent lack of concern shown by the Transportation Department.

A decision by the JTA at its May 1, 1975 meeting put off the sale of revenue bonds to finance the construction of the proposed bridge until some time the early part of 1976 because of lengthy bonding procedures.

Even though the authority had no assurance that revenue bonds for the Dames Point Bridge would be sold in 1976, at its August 19th meeting, it voted unanimously in the selection of the firm of Howard, Needles, Tammen and Bergendoff to design the bridge.

The first crack in the reasoning as to why the JTA selected the Dames Point Bridge as its first priority, appeared August 30, 1975 in *The Florida Times-Union* in a news story by James R. Ward, staff writer. Staff-writer Ward quoted James D. Ward, the State DOT district engineer as saying that Offshore Power Systems was promised the $137 million river crossing at Blount Island and given a first priority by the Jacksonville Transportation Authority. Engineer Ward said the city "promised to build a $137 million bridge to provide access to the plant's location. When OPS looked like a sure thing, then Dames Point became a No. 1 priority. Up to that time, I don't think the JTA had any priorities."

The next day, Wesley Paxson, the JTA chairman, said Ward was mistaken.

During the early part of December the *Jacksonville Journal* conducted a poll on the proposed bridge and though comments varied, more than 75 per cent of the people contacted opposed the construction of the Dames Point Bridge.

Ed Mueller, JTA executive director appearing at a meeting of city department heads on December 17, told Mayor Hans Tanzler that the traffic estimates of the Toups-Wemple firm were creating problems for the authority. According to the figures of the consultant, the Dames Point Bridge would have an average daily count by 1995 of 23,013 vehicles. "You can see how someone who is against the bridge can capitalize on this," Mueller said.

Ushering in the year of 1976, the drama continues.

January 2: Construction of the Dames Point Bridge would lock up the Jacksonville Transportation Authority's finances for years to come, eliminating the possibility of undertaking any other major project, unless bridge tolls are raised, JTA Chairman Wesley Paxson, says.

JTA member I.M. Sulzbacher agreed, saying it has been 12 years since the authority's last money-raising bond issue in 1963. "It was the growth in traffic and the toll increase (in 1973) that made it possible to finance this one," said Sulzbacher (*Jacksonville Journal*).

JTA Executive Director Ed Mueller said despite all the controversy surrounding the proposed Dames Point Bridge, he is "quite confident" that a $160 million bond issue will be successful. He said approval of Florida Legislature is expected in April and the Jacksonville City Council is now considering the JTA's request to pledge secondary gas tax revenues to support the bond issue (*Florida Times-Union*, January 31).

Ward Koutnik, transportation planner for the Jacksonville Area Planning Board, said by September 21st the current update of the Jacksonville Area Transportation Study will have produced information sufficient to support a decision relative whether to build the Dames Point Bridge (*Jacksonville Journal*, February 13).

Park Benjamin, a financial consultant of Lazard-Freres, New York told a City Council sub-committee that a $160 million bond issue for financing the Dames Point Bridge was financially feasible, even if earlier low traffic projections are used (*Jacksonville Journal*, February 25).

Department of Transportation District Engineer Walter Skinner said Southside Boulevard from Regency Square north to Merrill Road will be constructed even if the Dames Point Bridge is not built. He said the DOT probably would proceed with the northerly approach even if the bridge is not approved this year (*Jacksonville Journal*, March 15).

JTA Executive Director Ed Mueller said today the federal government's decision to require additional study of approaches to the proposed Dames Point Bridge will give the JTA time to rally public support for the project (*Jacksonville Journal*, April 15).

Financial consultants for the JTA are grappling with the Dames Point Bridge stumbling block of 12 years of projected deficits totaling $50.5 million. So far to date we haven't been able to get around these problems, JTA Executive Director Ed Mueller told the board yesterday (*Jacksonville Journal*, July 2).

JTA Chairman Wesley Paxson told the Northside Business Men's Club yesterday that the target date for opening the Dames Point Bridge was on July 1, 1981 (*Jacksonville Journal*, September 15).

During a meeting of businessmen, labor leaders and government officials, James Rinaman, a member of the JTA said throughout the history of Jacksonville's bridge building efforts, each new bridge has provided enough new revenues to double the previous bond issue. "What we are talking about with the Dames Point Bridge is putting ourselves in the position to double our money again in another 10 to 12 years. We've got a great big money-making machine in Jacksonville" (*Jacksonville Journal*, November 16).

The proposed Dames Point Bridge should be built because it is one of the "promises" that convinced Offshore Power Systems to locate in Jacksonville, contends OPS Vice President William J. Staten (*Jacksonville Journal*, November 18).

Realtor George M. Linville defended the city's efforts to attract Offshore Power Systems here, including assurances that the Dames Point Bridge would be built (*Jacksonville Journal*, November 18).

Alexander P. Zechella, president of Offshore Power Systems, said no promises ever were made by anyone to OPS officials to build a bridge to the company's facilities on Blount Island (*Florida Times-Union*, November 21).

Frank X. Friedmann, chairman of the Jacksonville Area Planning Board said Monday the board is not trying to get the JTA to delay plans for the Dames Point Bridge nor is the board trying to kill the bridge. "By March," Friedmann said, "we will have from our staff the information we need to make a decision on whether or not the Dames Point Bridge should or should not be constructed" (*Florida Times-Union*, November 23).

Council President Lynwood Roberts said in a letter to Jacksonville Area Chamber of Commerce President John McCormick that he has yet to see the proper economic information to allow him to justify the construction of the

Dames Point Bridge. "The public must be told more than the bridge is being built for OPS and to relieve five per cent to eight per cent of the traffic from the Mathews Bridge," Roberts said (*Florida Times-Union*, November 25).

Wesley Paxson, chairman of the JTA on December 22 told Mayor Hans Tanzler and city department heads that opponents of the Dames Point Bridge were trying to kill the project by delaying it until inflation makes it too costly to build (*Florida Times-Union*, December 23).

The year of 1977 brought forth the following exchanges:

Robert D. Barbour, a partner in Community Planning Consultants, Inc. at a forum sponsored by the Jacksonville Jaycees told the crowd he questioned the need for the Dames Point Bridge and predicted that if built it would encourage scattered, low density urban sprawl and undercut the city's opportunities for building a sophisticated mass transit system.

Later Barbour said "One of the most damaging things about the bridge is that by using the JTA's figures, their projected traffic volumes, the bridge could never even pay the interest on the $170 million bond issue, much less the principal" (*Jacksonville Journal*, January 15).

Governor Reubin Askew has suggested that the State Department of Transportation have an outside consultant review the construction cost estimates of the Dames Point Bridge (*Jacksonville Journal*, January 15).

JTA Chairman Wesley Paxson emphasized that the main reason for the Dames Point Bridge is to meet the city's future transportation needs. "We feel the need for the bridge is realistic," Paxson told the Jacksonville Board of Realtors. "We do feel the financing is feasible. The financial plan was designed not to use (city's secondary) gas tax" (*Jacksonville Journal*, January 21).

Jim Rinaman, JTA member said that Jacksonville's toll bridges are "a money-making machine" that will make it possible to improve the local transportation system for many years to come. "The only reason we have it is we were 15 years ahead of other places" (*Jacksonville Journal*, February 22).

State Representative Steve Pajcic said private enterprise would not build the Dames Point Bridge. "It simply isn't profitable. There are too many guesses, estimates and unknowns" (*Jacksonville Journal*, February 22).

Ward Koutnik, transportation planner for the Jacksonville Area Planning Board, told the City Council finance committee the Dames Point Bridge is a conservatively planned project that will encounter no financial difficulties even if the revenues from the city's bridge system are only 80 per cent of what has been projected by JTA consultants.

Under the questioning by Joe Carlucci, city councilman, Koutnik admitted that the bridge is not his No. 1 priority for solving the existing traffic problems in the city. Koutnik said, "If you want an answer to what we should do to solve our existing traffic problems, it's not going to be to build the Dames Point Bridge" (*Jacksonville Journal*, March 2).

Dr. Louis A. Woods, assistant professor of economics and geography at the University of North Florida, questions the validity of the Jacksonville Area Chamber of Commerce's economic study of the Dames Point Bridge. Woods said the study failed to consider the growth that would take place in Northside without the bridge. "To attribute it all to the bridge is erroneous, which I find sort of flaky" (*Jacksonville Journal*, March 21).

Jacksonville City Council pledged 100 per cent of the city's secondary gasoline tax revenue to support the $160 million bond issue for the Dames Point Bridge project (*Jacksonville Journal*, March 23).

The Duval County legislative delegation by a vote of 9-4 approved the sale of a $177 million bond issue for the Dames Point Bridge (*Florida Times-Union*, March 26).

The Jacksonville Transportation Authority unanimously approved hiring the engineering firm of Howard, Needles, Tammen and Bergendoff to draw final engineering plans for the Dames Point Bridge (*Florida Times-Union*, April 8).

Governor Reubin Askew endorsed construction of the Dames Point Bridge and said present plans for building it provide safeguards for the state (*Florida Times-Union*, April 30).

Economist Marvin R. Edwards, president of the consulting firm Edwards and Edwards Investment Counselors, has written the House and Senate transportation committees asking legislators to turn aside "pork barrel reciprocity" and vote against the Dames Point Bridge. He said in his letter that evaluation of the Dames Point Bridge is, "difficult because so many sets of figures and projections have been given by the bridge proponents" (*Jacksonville Journal*, May 2).

Julia B. Brumley, president of the Arlington East Civic Association said she is concerned a toll increase would be necessary if the Jacksonville Transportation Authority builds the Dames Point Bridge under the terms of a bill being considered by the Florida House Transportation Committee (*Jacksonville Journal*, May 13).

A bill which pledges the state's full faith and credit and a covenant to complete the Dames Point Bridge was passed by both Houses of Legislature (*Jacksonville Journal*, June 3).

By a vote of 15-3 the City Council reaffirmed an earlier decision to support issuance of $160 million in bonds for construction of the Dames Point Bridge, backed by toll revenues and the city's share of the secondary gasoline tax (*Florida Times-Union*, October 25).

Jack Dent of the engineering firm of Sverdrup and Parcel and Associates reported to the JTA that permits will be needed from the Coast Guard and the Florida Department of Environmental Regulation to build the Dames Point Bridge. He said the applications have been filed and there is no particular problem expected in obtaining the permits (*Jacksonville Journal*, November 16).

The Arlington East Civic Association, Julia Brumley, Mrs. Jessie Perry, Anne and Bob Grimes, J.S. Boulton as president of the St. Johns River Bar Pilots Association, Duval Audubon Society and Florida Audubon Society requested that Governor Reubin Askew and the Cabinet order a hearing before considering approval of the $160 million bond issue sought for the Dames Point Bridge project by the Jacksonville Transportation Authority (*Florida Times-Union*, December 18).

C. Harold McCarthy, president of Jacksonville Maritime Association, said association members voted 29-5 to publicly oppose the Dames Point Bridge, as being too hazardous (*Florida Times-Union*, December 2).

For 1978, more controversy.

Mayor Hans Tanzler told the Northside Business Men's Club that Florida Attorney General Robert Shevin is tuned in to a political applause meter, and because of that, could kill off the Dames Point Bridge (*Florida Times-Union*, January 11).

At a meeting of the Rotary Club of West Jacksonville at the Ramada Inn West, Wesley Paxson, chairman of the JTA said critics of the Dames Point Bridge have a right to criticize the $165 million project, but they ought to deal in facts rather than attack the credibility of the agencies and individuals involved (*Florida Times-Union*, January 12).

Ken Tucker, Attorney General Robert Shevin's cabinet aide, said March 21 is now the earliest date at which the Cabinet is likely to consider the Dames Point Bridge. He said Cabinet members still haven't received reports on the bridge's traffic and revenue projections (*Jacksonville Journal*, January 20).

Mayor Hans Tanzler accused Attorney General Robert Shevin of playing politics in finding the Cabinet should consider all issues including environmental questions in reviewing Dames Point Bridge bonds (*Florida Times-Union*, Janaury 31).

The State Department of Transportation raised its estimate on the cost of the Danes Point Bridge by $13.4 million to a total cost of $153.2 million.

Senate President Lew Brantley said he did not know what the effect of the escalation would be on the project, but conceded it could not help.

Brantley said, "I guess the governor and Cabinet will decide the fiscal sufficiency in April" (*Florida Times-Union*, February 14).

Traffic consultant Ed Wemple has advised the JTA that he will not submit a "final traffic and revenue report" to use in selling bonds to finance the Dames

Point Bridge until he has had a chance to analyze the impact of the opening of Interstate 295 (*Jacksonville Journal*, March 2).

James R. Ward, *Times-Union* staff writer in the March 7 issue wrote as follows:

The Jacksonville Urban Transportation Study policy committee wants the 1978 Legislature to approve a new covenant-to-complete bill to ensure the inclusion of proposed Florida 9-A as an integral part of the Dames Point Bridge connector system.

The JUATS policy committee also wants the Duval County legislative delegation to seek a $10 million grant from the state to permit the Florida Department of Transportation to construct a section of Florida 9-A from its now-proposed terminus to Monument Road to Atlantic Boulevard at St. Johns Bluff Road.

The committee unanimously approved these two stipulations after a special meeting Monday afternoon at the offices of the Jacksonville Transportation Authority after studying a resolution presented to JUATS and the JTA by the Greater Arlington Civic Council, which represents 17 civic organizations and some 85,000 Arlington area residents.

I.M. Sulzbacher, president of the Deerwood Residents' Association, and Robert Adams, president of the council, indicated that if the present covenant to complete was not amended or rewritten entirely to include Florida 9A as one leg of the Dames Point Freeway's southerly connector, the council would oppose the $160 million bond issue before the Florida Cabinet April 13-14.

Wesley Paxson, JTA chairman appearing before the House Transportation Committee on March 27 was unable to explain why two documents he gave to the committee relating to the same traffic and revenue projections on the Dames Point Bridge contained different figures (*Jacksonville Journal,* March 28).

Governor Reubin Askew and the Florida Cabinet yesterday, by a 6-1 vote approved the pledging of the full faith and credit of the state to a $140 million bond issue for the Dames Point Bridge (*Florida Times-Union*, April 14).

Edward Hildago, assistant secretary of the Navy, yesterday in a letter to Rep. Charles E. Bennett said the Navy wants the height of the proposed Dames Point Bridge raised to 160 feet across the entire channel and Admiral James L. Holloway III, chief of Naval operations, notified the Coast Guard, which will hold a hearing on the granting of a bridge permit next month (*Florida Times-Union*, May 26).

Bob Adams, president of the Greater Arlington Civic Council announced the council has dropped its objections to the Dames Point Bridge because it now has "written assurances" other roadwork will be done, preventing traffic congestion at the Arlington triangle when the bridge opens (*Jacksonville Journal*, June 30).

The Arlington East Civic Association and five local residents say they will appeal the decision by Leon County Circuit Court Judge James L. Joanos validating $140 million in bonds to build the Dames Point Bridge. Julia A. Brumley, president of the Civic Association said, "Coming in we were prepared to appeal" (*Jacksonville Journal*, July 6).

Arnold P. McIlwain, the Port of Jacksonville Maritime Ad Hoc Committee's co-chairman, says the group will fight issuance of a Coast Guard permit for the Dames Point Bridge, even with the maximum vertical clearance increased from 152 to 160.9 feet (*Jacksonville Journal*, July 10).

Joe Porricelli, a partner in Engineering Computer Opt-economics, Inc., told the Florida Cabinet in April that because of the Dames Point Bridge's location in a tight turn, the structure constitutes a serious danger to shipping and to motorists using the bridge. He said the only solution to the problem would be to remove the bridge piers from the river and place them on dry land (*Jacksonville Journal*, October 9).

During the Coast Guard's public hearing on the Dames Point Bridge, those testifying in favor of the issuance of the Coast Guard permit were John H. Leeper with the maritime consulting firm of Simat, Helliesen and Eicher; naval architect Robert J. Rapscott with George C. Sharp Inc., and G. Gordon Samis, president of G. Gordon Samis and Associates, naval architects (*Jacksonville Journal*, November 7).

At the continued Coast Guard hearing in the Parker High School auditorium Wednesday, November 8, Captain Joe Bolton, a river pilot said at least five ships have run aground in the St. Johns River during the past 10 years near the planned location of the south supporting pier of the Dames Point Bridge.

William Birchfield, chairman of the JTA stated that if the bonds to build the Dames Point Bridge are not sold by the end of next September, the authority might have to cut the bridge from six lanes to four or sell additional bonds (*Florida Times-Union*, December 21).

The beginning of the end in 1979

Attorney David Gluckman, representing a group of Dames Point Bridge opponents, at a hearing in Tallahassee, on environmental aspects of the bridge, charged that the Florida Department of Environmental Regulations would violate its own rules governing complex source permits if approval were granted. He closely questioned the testimony by Jay Fearnside, state design traffic engineer, that the bridge would relieve traffic congestion in the downtown area by diverting through traffic away from the central city.

Gluckman asked Fearnside how he felt about the report of the Jacksonville Area Planning Board which contained the statement: "Very little traffic unnecessarily passes through the central business district."

"I don't agree with it totally," Fearnside said, "I can't totally disagree" (*Jacksonville Journal*, January 9).

Bill Birchfield, JTA chairman in Tallahassee, told the legislators on February 5 that the state could pay more than $20 million over an eight-year period to fund cost overruns on the Dames Point Bridge. Birchfield said because of lawsuits against the bridge and the waiting time for the required Coast Guard permit, he had no prediction about when the bonds can be sold (*Jacksonville Journal*, February 6).

James Rinaman, JTA member predicted the authority could withstand the cost of another year's delay on the Dames Point Bridge project (*Jacksonville Journal*, April 25).

Fred Jones, House transportation chairman, said yesterday, building connector roads for the Dames Point Bridge would use up all the primary road improvement funds for 17 counties of northeast Florida for more than two years (*Florida Times-Union*, May 3).

City Councilman Clarence Suggs, worried about the declining toll revenues collected by the JTA, plans to have the Public Services Committee, which he heads, study the feasibility of the Dames Point Bridge project (*Jacksonville Journal*, June 22).

The Jacksonville Transportation Authority at its meeting today voted unanimously to advertise for bids for construction of the Dames Point Bridge project with an opening date of October 4 (*Jacksonville Journal*, July 12).

Marvin R. Edwards, economic consultant said, "City Council's continued support of the Dames Point Bridge will demonstrate that special interest groups still have a stranglehold on Jacksonville, 12 years after consolidation" (*Jacksonville Journal*, August 7).

A complaint, prepared by attorneys Thomas M. Baumer and Guy O. Farmer, with the law firm of Mahoney, Hadlow and Adams, was filed today in the U.S. district court asking the federal court to declare invalid the bridge permit issued to the Jacksonville Transportation Authority July 11 by Coast Guard Commandant Adm. J.B. Hayes (*Jacksonville Journal*, August 23).

Mayor Jake Godbold said Monday he does not want another dime spent on feeder roads to the Dames Point Bridge until officials are sure the bridge will be built and the total cost determined (*Florida Times-Union*, October 2).

A *Times-Union* examination of the Dames Point Bridge and related road projects shows an estimated $271.3 million will be needed to build the proposed bridge and its connecting roads (*Florida Times-Union*, October 2).

The JTA yesterday authorized completion of engineering and design work on the north and south approaches to the Dames Point Bridge (*Florida Times-Union*, November 20).

JTA Chairman Bill Birchfield told the Bold City Jaycees at a luncheon meeting held yesterday, the JTA was preparing to start construction of the Dames Point Bridge (*Florida Times-Union*, November 30).

Anne Grimes, newly appointed member of the JTA by Governor Bob Graham, said she will continue to oppose construction of the Dames Point Bridge (*Florida Times-Union*, December 15).

The end in 1980

During a meeting of the House Transportation Committee, which is conducting a review of bonding covenants authorized by the Legislature and the Cabinet, Walter Skinner DOT district engineer was questioned by Rep. Peter Dunbar, relative to an estimated $36 million above estimates on the cost of the Dames Point Bridge project given to the Legislature and Cabinet in 1977. Skinner and his assistants agreed with figures showing the bridge right now is estimated to cost $36 million above estimates given to the Legislature and Cabinet to gain their approval (*Jacksonville Journal*, January 8).

State DOT District Engineer Walter Skinner assured the House Transportation Committee on Tuesday that the Dames Point Bridge project does not commit the state to complete the eastern bypass at any time in the foreseeable future. "There is no obligation to complete it," Skinner told a skeptical Rep. Fred Jones, chairman of the committee (*Florida Times-Union*, January 9).

The JTA today approved a resolution asserting the projected costs of building the Dames Point Bridge will not exceed projected revenues (*Jacksonville Journal*, February 21).

Edward Wemple, president of Vollmer-Wemple Consulting Engineers, Inc. of New York recommended Thursday to the JTA a 75-cent toll for the proposed Dames Point Bridge instead of the 50-cents estimated earlier (*Florida Times-Union*, February 22).

Jacksonville City Councilman Eric Smith says he is not surprised by a JTA consultant's recommendation to raise tolls on all existing bridges to pay for the construction of the Dames Point Bridge, despite years of promises that step would never be taken.

Letters to Smith from JTA Chairman Bill Birchfield and former Chairman Wesley Paxson said: "Our approach has been and will continue to be to fund the project within our existing revenue base and accordingly there is no intention to increase the present toll or to do away with the commuter ticket book" (*Jacksonville Journal*, February 26).

JTA Chairman Bill Birchfield indicated Friday the Wall Street bond market had put the Dames Point Bridge beyond the financial reach of the state of Florida.

He said he would announce at a news conference Monday whether the JTA would continue to push for the bridge, but he said he was giving serious consideration to postponing efforts to sell the bonds that would pay for the bridge (*Florida Times-Union*, March 22).

Bill Birchfield, JTA chairman, on March 22 released a statement saying high interest rates on the kinds of bonds needed to pay for the Dames Point Bridge had made the $140 million project impractical.

The statement said, "The JTA cannot pursue the sale of the bonds for the Dames Point Bridge right now. Prudence dictates that we suspend those efforts. "

"I have not consulted other board members. If the board wants to overturn my decision, it is up to them" (*Florida Times-Union*, March 23).

The JTA on Tuesday approved a new $140 million financing plan for building the Dames Point Bridge. Those voting for the financial plan, prepared by the consulting firm of Lazard Freres & Co., without even asking to see it, were members R. Lee Smith, Walter Skinner, Arnold Tritt, Andrew Robinson and James Deaton.

Anne Grimes cast the only negative vote.

Chairman Bill Birchfield also cast an affirmative vote for the plan (*Jacksonville Journal*, June 11).

On June 13, a Florida Department of Transportation report said the state had only $17.7 million to build the north connector to the Dames Point Bridge, which transportation experts figured would cost $25.2 million.

Because of the report, the bridge was removed from the agenda for Tuesday's meeting of the governor and Cabinet.

Earlier in the week, JTA Chairman Bill Birchfield told Cabinet aides the project could not be built if not given state approval Tuesday. He said "a vote to delay is a vote to kill."

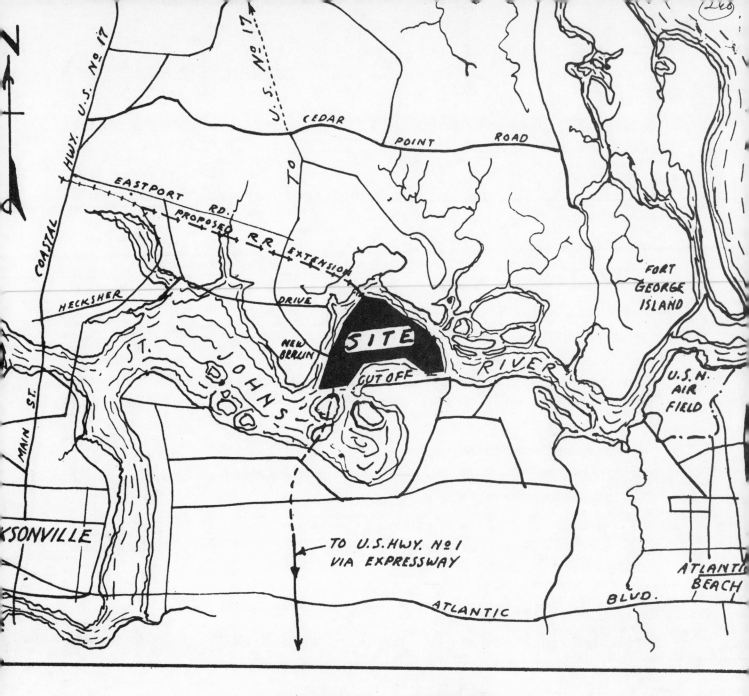

AREA MAP

SCALE IN MILES

0 1 2 3 4 5

PORT & INDUSTRIAL DEVELOPMENT

DUVAL COUNTY, FLORIDA

WILLIAM G. BUECHELER
CONSULTING ENGINEER
Registered No. 3777

1031 LAKE FOREST BLVD.   JACKSONVILLE, F

ARTHUR N. LEE
CONSULTANT

Drawn July 15, 1955 by William G. Buech

Southeast
Section of
Duval County
in 1955

Revised to July 25th, 1955

CHAPTER XXX
THE PROPOSED DAMES POINT BRIDGE — PHASE ONE - A REVIEW

Why did not the proposed Dames Point Bridge project succeed?

This question has a multitude of answers, some pertinent and some borderline.

A poll of knowledgeable citizens reveals responses as follows:

1. The project was premature and should not have been a first priority.

2. Some members of the JTA at times seem to have had a personal interest in the project — others as to whether or where the project should be built.

3. JTA members prior to the 1957 and 1963 bond issues made rare public appearances, whereas for the proposed Dames Point Bridge bond issue many JTA members were constantly making public appearances, calling for support of the bridge project.

4. General public support for the project was considerably diminished due to the publicized alleged promise to company officials by certain public officials of the City of Jacksonville, JTA and the State of Florida to build a bridge over the St. Johns River at a specified location, as an inducement to the company to locate in Duval County.

5. The merits of the project were often lost, in that there were too many contradictions in projected traffic counts and expected revenues.

6. The Jacksonville Area Planning Board and Government Environmental Regulations, with their theoretical requirements and demands, caused years of delay.

7. The JTA was utterly naive in starting the project, thinking the state and federal government could be relied upon to keep promises or commitments.

8. There were too many unsubstantiated, conflicting and exaggerated statements made by a few authority members.

9. JTA financial consultants were unwilling partners in the coup d'etat that sounded the death knell of the immediate start of the project.

10. The JTA spent millions of dollars on the design of the Dames Point Bridge, without the benefit of appropriate revenue bond funds, when such expenditures should have been used to eliminate certain hazardous and dangerous segments now existing on J. Turner Butler Boulevard.

11. The Arlington and Beaches citizens who assume a Dames Point Bridge will relieve existing traffic congestion on the Mathews Bridge, will be disappointed for, without another east-west bridge traffic projections indicate congestion will continue to escalate on the existing bridge.

12.   In order for the Dames Point Bridge Project to become a reality the public should be given factual data based solely upon verifiable figures and calculations of its engineers and financial advisors.

In the final analysis, as the curtain closed on Phase I, there were no winners, but losers who were the people of Duval County.

The traveling public of this community continued to lose when Mayor Hans Tanzler on October 15, 1970, following the recommendation of William K. Jackson, chairman of the Jacksonville Area Planning Board, wrote to Roger L. Main, chairman of the JTA requesting that the authority discontinue its planning.

The request by Tanzler was a new and unique type of action, for it was the first time since the JTA began to function as an agency of the State that it was asked to cease its planning of expressway projects.

It was just another example of outside forces hindering the JTA from doing their job properly.

Unless there is a reversal in the influence of outside forces, then the JTA will remain a spoke in the spinning wheel of political whims, decisions and aspirations.

YESTERYEARS, TODAY AND TOMORROW

What does the future hold for Duval County? What may we expect in the year of 2000 in the way of transportation? Are such queries hard to answer? Will it be pure guesswork to give predictions of what our grandchildren may enjoy? No, for all one has to do is turn back the pages of history to the early 20's to visualize and glimpse what the citizens of Duval County and Jacksonville experienced in their way of life.

Everything was taken leisurely in those days. There was no hurry. If one wanted to take a train, one went to the intersection of Bay and Main Streets and got a hack for a mere 25 cents. A polite black driver, all bedecked in the finery of his day and driving a one-horse buggy, would take you to Union Station. And if one wanted to take a holiday outing "way out in the country", Ortega was the place most people thought of in those days. A streetcar would bounce over the poorly laid tracks and possibly an hour or an hour and a half later one could get off the open streetcar and enjoy a full day's outing. But one would be sure to time the return to Jacksonville in the early afternoon hours as no night streetcars made the perilous journey. Those who cared to go to the beach, whether by Hupmobile, Maxwell, Pierce Arrow or any other make of car, would first cross the St. Johns River on the ferry boat Duval and then drive over a narrow brick road for fifty minutes. On holidays, particularly the Fourth of July, Florida East Coast Railway ran "specials" where one could ride jammed in coaches to the beaches and be glad to arrive safely in an hour, as stops to pick up passengers were made at South Jacksonville, Spring Park, Hogan, Center Park and San Pablo.

And what of the return trip? From Atlantic Beach to Jacksonville, a two hour run would be par for the course, for the engine could barely move with an additional eight coaches filled to capacity. Of course, passengers got off at San Pablo, Spring Park, Hogan and South Jacksonville before the final stop at Union Station on West Bay Street.

Who in the days of 1920 would visualize or even dare to predict that by 1982 one could whizz over the St. Johns River in a matter of minutes, could journey to the beaches in a record time of twenty five minutes, could go to the Ortega area within fifteen minutes. No, it would have been hard to believe this could materialize within the span of 60 years. So, what have we today?

An Expressway has been built, additions and improvements are always underway. Five highway bridges are spanning the St. Johns River to take care of the ever increasing flow of traffic.

The Airport, with all its modern facilities located between Interstate 95 and Lem Turner Road, can be reached from any place in Jacksonville within forty minutes, whereas even twenty-five years ago such a trip would consume more than an hour. It also may be easily reached by splendid highways from neighboring Georgia, central Florida and the East Coast. With all this progress in transportation within the memory of man, then who is to say similar and comparable improvements having far more reaching effects will not be built by the year of 2000? Let us then prophesy to see what the citizens of Duval County may expect to accept as a matter of course in the way of transportation in the glorious year of 2000. Of course, in the meantime, a great residential area of Duval County will have been built between the St. Johns River and the Atlantic Ocean and the industrial complex of the County will be in the northwest and northeast quadrants. The Federal Government in the meantime, will have expanded its Naval Facilities in the southwest which will definitely limit and confine the residential area in that section.

The beaches of Duval County will be the haven of those transported northern citizens who have cast their lot in the County and can enjoy, daily, the wide, vast expanse of beaches extending from the St. Johns River southerly to St. Augustine, and the greater Mandarin area will have grown to a population of over 80,000.

During the course of years, existing highways will have been improved, overcrossings at major intersections will be constructed and Duval County can be proud of an integrated system of expressways and limited access throughways constructed for mass transportation as well as for the automobile and truck. Truly the system will be the envy of most progressive cities of the South.

It was indeed a frightening thought to many citizens in 1950 when a $28. million revenue Bond Issue was proposed to finance an expressway system in Duval County. By 1955, hardly an eyebrow was lifted when a new refunding issue of $70. million was suggested to the public. And again in 1963, when a vast new program of expansion and additions to the existing expressway system was planned calling for an issue of $135. million in revenue bonds, the general public's response was almost unanimously in accord, excepting, of course, the less than a handcount of people who for reasons known only to themselves, raised a voice in opposition.

As to the future: There will be other bond issues and as time passes and with the population of Duval County approaching the million mark, the issuance of revenue bonds for transportation facilities will be accepted as casually as one does in financing his car or house. Who, today, can say that a $400. million revenue bond issue by 1999 will not be a reality?

Selective Name Index
Number Denotes Chapter

A

Acosta, Edward I. 11, 15
Adams, Bob 29
Aiken, Harold 19, 20
Akra, Vincent 19
Allen, J. H. 8
Ambrose, Karl 29
Anderson, Leon 21, 22
Angus, Robert 8, 11
Askew, Reubin 29
Atwood, J. K. 15, 16

B

Bailey, Cecil. C. 19, 20
Baldwin, Charles 21
Barfield, William D. 21, 22
Barbour, Robert D. 29
Baskin, H. H. 9, 10
Baumer, Thomas M. 29
Baxley, Al R. 29
Bayless, Elgin F. 7, 9, 10
Bayley, Ted 6
Belote, W. Howard 19, 20
Bennett, Charles E. 29
Benjamin, Park 29
Birchfield, William 29
Blankenship, D. S. 15
Blount, J. Henry 6, 11
Blum, Charles W. 15
Blume, George 6
Bockledge, William 19
Bolsch, Al 11
Bolton, Lee 29
Boulton, J. S. 29
Boyd, James E. 6
Brantley, Lew 29
Brest, Alexander 19
Brewer, J.A. 19, 21, 23, 28
Brown, A. T. 24
Brown, A. E. 25
Brumley, Julia B. 29
Bryant, Farris 19, 20, 21
Buck, B. C. 24
Buck, Lucius ... 18,19,20,21,27,28
Bunnell, Ed 21
Burns, Haydon 15, 16
Burrell, Maynard 8

Butler, J. Turner 11, 12, 15

C

Cagle, Floyd 20
Caldwell, Millard F. 9, 10
Cannon, Clyde 6
Cannon, Phillip 20
Carey, Jefferson 20, 21
Carlton, Mabry 11, 24
Carlucci, Joe 29
Carrison, H. George 22
Cesary, William 24
Church, H. C. 19
Cockrell, Alston 24
Collins, LeRoy 16, 17, 18, 19
Conner, M. A. 19, 21, 23
Coppedge, W. T. Sr. 21
Cowart, Walter 21
Craig, James C. 19
Crain, Joseph P. 20
Croasdell, Rex 9, 11
Crosby, John 19, 21, 22
Cullum, C. Moody 21

D

Daniels, Walter G. ... 11, 15, 16
Davis, Vernon 21
Dean, W. E. 15
Deaton, James 29
Dent, Jack 21, 29
D'Amico, Salvatore 28
Dixon, Earl 29
Doyle, John P. 27
Drenning, W. C. 21
Dunbar, Peter 29
Dunivan, Robert 21
Dunlop, C. D. 19, 21
Durden, William 21
Duss, John S. III 19

E

Edmunds, Ollie 29
Edwards, Marvin R. 29
Ekey, F. W. 21

F

Fant, Julian 27

Farmer, Guy 29
Fearnside, Jay 29
Fewell, John 21
Fewell, Jennifer 21
Fifield, Stephen 6
Fish, George 24
Fletcher, Duncan U. 5
Foerster, David W. 19, 21
Fozzard, Harry B. 19
Friedman, Frank X. 29

G

Gast, James 21
Gibbs, George W. 8
Gluckman, David 29
Goldbold, Jake 29
Goodrich, L. E. 6
Gordon, Robert D. 11, 14
Greene,
C. Ray Sr. 11,15,19,21,22
Greene, C. Ray Jr. 19
Green, J. C. 21
Green, Richey 14
Grimes, Anne 29
Grimes, Bob 29
Guernsey, S. Kendrick 8, 9
Guyton, Joseph W. 27

H

Hadlow, Earl 27
Hammond, Joe F. ... 6,8,11,15,24
Hardwick, Cheevar 19, 20
Harrell, John W. 24
Harris, Bob 21, 22
Hazelden, Ernest S. 15, 16
Heldt, Henning 6
Hemphill, Edward S. 19
Henson, W. E. 20
Herlong, Charles W. 24
Hildago, Edward 29
Hill, Marvin 27
Hills, George B. 15
Hobbs, Ed 11
Hodges, George H. Sr. 19
Hoffman, Charles 21
Holland, Spessard 24
Holloway, James L. III 29

Hopkins, Charles 19, 20
Horne, Chalmers D. 21
Howard, Harry 11
Huddleston, P. M. .. 15,19,20,21
Hunter, Donald E. 27

I

Imeson, T. C. 6, 8

J

Jackson, Warren B. 20
Jackson, William K. 27, 30
Johns, Charles E. 15
Johnson, Charles M. 11, 12
Johnson, Charles W. 21
Johnson, Cleveland 11
Johnson, Francis 24
Johnson, William 11
Jones, Earl 6, 11
Jones, Fred 29
Jones, Mary Virginia 24
Jones, Wilbur E. ... 17, 18, 19, 28
Joseph, James A. 22

K

Kennedy, J. Dillon 15, 16, 20
Kent, Fred 15, 16
Kirk, Claude 21
Koger, Ira M. 16
Koutnik, Ward 24
Kynes, James 21, 22

L

Langley, E. Robert 1, 4
Langston, Carl D. 11
Leeper, John H. 29
Lechner, Robert C. 11
Linville, George M. 29
Littlefield, Winston 21
Lloyd, J. Saxton 15
Lochner, W. H. 18
Lockwood, Langdon 12

Long, J. A. 4
Luce, Earle P. 1, 4
Luckie, Charles A. 11

M

Macdonald, Eugene 15
Mahon, W. Lacy 16, 18, 19
Main, Roger L. 21, 23, 27, 30
Maness, William H. 18, 19
Marshall, Sam 21
Marshall, Tom 6, 8, 10, 11
Mathews,
John E. Sr. 8, 9, 11, 15, 16, 24
Mathews, Mrs. John E. Sr. ... 15
Mayo, William 21
McArthur, D. W. 24
McCarthy, C. Harold 29
McCarty, Dan 15
McCormick, John 29
McGinty, Paul 27
McIlwain, Arnold P. 29
McKethan,
Alfred A. 11,12,14,15
Mellinger, Erwin 6
Meyer, Roland 11
Milam, Robert R. 8
Monahan, James T. 15
Monroe, S. L. 11
Moore, Jack 19
Morgan,
Fletcher 11,15,16,18,19,21
Mueller, Edward 21, 23, 29
Mulcahy, Edward F. 19

N

Naughton, Daniel A. 21
Newkirk, Arthur 11

O

Ogden, Carl 29
O'Reilly,
James H. 18, 19, 20, 21
Osborne, Frank K. 21

Overman, C. H. 9, 10
Overstreet, H. W. 21

P

Page, William W. 29
Pajcic, Steve 29
Parker, W. M. 8
Paxson, Wesley C. 23, 29
Peeler, James M. 15
Pemberton, Irvin J. 18, 19
Penman, Arthur 24
Perkins, Otis 27
Perry, Jessie 29
Peterson, W. C. 28
Phillips, T. T. 6
Philips, Ben J. 16
Pierce, Carrison, Wulbern ... 18
Pitts Brothers 4
Porricelli, Joe 29
Poucher, Allen 8
Powell, George M. 24
Powers, Earl P. 17, 18, 19
Powers, Ralph 21, 22
Priddy, T. R. 20, 21
Prince, T. C. 6

R

Raulerson, L. A. 8, 11
Register, J. Alvin 21
Reynolds, John F. 15
Reynolds,
Smith & Hills 16, 18, 21, 29
Richardson, Ray 22
Rinaman, James 29
Roberts, Lynwood 27, 29
Robinson, Andrew 29

S

Samis, G. Gordon 29
Sanders, Lester 21
Schmidt, Gert 23
Scholtz, Dave 5

Schroder, Roy 6

Schultz, Frederick H. 21, 23

Scruby, Frank M. 21

Senn, R. I. 15

Selber, Philip N. 19

Sheddan, W. E. .. 6, 11, 15, 16, 25

Sherman, Frank W. 8

Shevin, Robert 29

Simmons, Guy 16

Simmons, W. B. 25

Simons, George 6

Simpson, L. M. Mrs. 16

Simpson, Richard 16

Sirmans, Gordon H. 28

Skinner, A. Chester Sr. 24

Skinner, A. Chester Jr. 24

Skinner Brightman 24

Skinner, B. J. 24

Skinner, Ben 24

Skinner, J. F. 24

Skinner, Richard G. 24

Skinner, W. D. 24

Skinner, Walter 29

Smathers, Bruce 29

Smith, Claude Jr. 16

Smith, Eric 29

Smith, R. Lee 29

Smith, Roy E. 21

Smith, W. Gregory 16

Smith, Vernon 20

Sollee, Arthur N. Sr.
...... 5,6,8,11,15,16,17,19,21,22,
23,27,28

Solohub, J. V. 20, 21

Spaulding, Ralph 8, 25

Stack, Fred 24

Stanly, Richard L. 19, 21

Staten, William J. 29

Steeg, Stewart B. 21

Steele, Henry A. 29

Stevenson, Edward Lee 24

Stockton, Gilchrist 6

Stockton, James R. 8

Suggs, Clarence 29

Sulzbacher, I. M. 29

Sverdrup & Parcel 21, 29

Sweat, Wesley 16, 19

Sweisgood, William 21

T

Tanzler, Hans 23, 27, 29, 30

Taylor, Carl M. 15, 16

Taylor, Dodge 11

Taylor, Glover J. 11, 14, 15

Teale, Willis E. 5

Thomas, Charles 19

Tocknell, Stephen 27

Tolbert, Mike 8

Tritt, Arnold 29

Tucker, Ken 29

Turner, George E. 19

V

Valz, Fred M. 6

W

Walker, Jimmie 20

Walker, J. P. 8

Walker, Jonny 16

Ward, James D. 21, 29

Ward, James R. 29

Warren, Fuller 11

Warren, Julian 21

Webb, Cecil 16

Weil, Nathan 6

Wemple, Edward 21, 29

West, Arthur L. 19

Westberry,
Harry W. 16, 18, 19

Whatley,
Brown L. 8, 9, 11, 14, 15, 16

Whitehead, C. Frank 1, 11

Whitehead, Harold 8

White, Moss L. 8

Woods, Louis A. 29

Wright, Thomas 19, 21

Y

Yates, Paul R. S. 28

Young, George C. 19

Young, Frank 27

Z

Zechella, Alexander P. 29